P9-CLA-940

The Concept of Race

The Concept of Race

Edited by Ashley Montagu

Collier Books

Collier-Macmillan Limited, London

COPYRIGHT © 1964 BY ASHLEY MONTAGU

All rights reserved. No part of this book may be
reproduced or transmitted in any form or by any means,
electronic or mechanical, including photocopying,
recording or by any information storage and retrieval
system, without permission in writing from the Publisher.

Library of Congress Catalog Card Number: 64-20310

FIRST COLLIER BOOKS EDITION 1969

The Concept of Race is published in a hardcover
edition by The Free Press, New York

The Macmillan Company
Collier-Macmillan Canada Ltd., Toronto, Ontario

Printed in the United States of America

To
BERN DIBNER
and to the memory of
MANFRED LOWEN
(1925–1949)

CONTRIBUTORS

ROBERT T. ANDERSON, Assistant Professor of Anthropology, Mills College, Oakland, California.

NIGEL A. BARNICOT, Professor of Physical Anthropology, University College, University of London.

C. LORING BRACE, Assistant Professor of Anthropology, University of California at Santa Barbara, California.

PAUL R. EHRLICH, Associate Professor of Zoology, Department of Biological Sciences, Stanford University, Stanford, California.

JEAN HIERNAUX, Maître de Recherche, Centre National de la Recherche Scientifique, France.

LANCELOT HOGBEN, Professor Emeritus of Medical Statistic, University of Birmingham, Birmingham, England.

RICHARD W. HOLM, Associate Professor of Zoology, Department of Biological Sciences, Stanford University, Stanford, California.

FRANK B. LIVINGSTONE, Associate Professor of Anthropology, University of Michigan, Ann Arbor, Michigan.

ASHLEY MONTAGU, Formerly Professor of Anthropology, Rutgers University, New Brunswick, New Jersey.

S. L. WASHBURN, Professor of Anthropology, University of California, Berkeley, California.

Ethnology is the science which determines the distinctive characters of the persistent modifications of mankind; which ascertains the distribution of those modifications in present and past times, and seeks to discover the causes, or conditions of existence, both of the modifications and of their distribution. I say "persistent" modifications, because, unless incidentally, ethnology has nothing to do with chance and transitory peculiarities of human structure. And I speak of "persistent modifications" or "stocks" rather than of "varieties," or "races," or "species," because each of these last well-known terms implies, on the part of its employer, a preconceived opinion touching one of those problems, the solution of which is the ultimate object of the science; and in regard to which, therefore, ethnologists are especially bound to keep their minds open and their judgments freely balanced.

THOMAS HENRY HUXLEY
On The Methods and Results of Ethnology, 1865

CONTENTS

Introduction

The contributions to this volume have been written by seven physical anthropologists and three anthropologically sophisticated biologists. The concept of race examined in this volume is the concept of race that physical anthropologists have, in common with most biologists, worked with and subscribed to. It is the biological concept of race which is the subject of critical examination in this book.

Most readers will be aware that the social (sometimes miscalled the "sociological") concept of race, the doctrine, to put it briefly, that there exist superior and inferior races, has long been unacceptable to anthropologists. What most readers may not be aware of is the fact that the biological concept of race has become unacceptable to a growing number of biologists on the one hand and to an equally increasing number of physical anthropologists on the other. The biological concept of race has it that within a particular species there exist different populations of the same species which are distinguished from one another by the possession of certain distinctive hereditary traits. Whatever form this definition may take this is the concept of race to which most biologists and most physical anthropologists at the present time still subscribe. In the present volume it is this concept of race with particular reference to its usage by the physical anthropologists that is the special focus of our critical examination.

The history of science is littered with the relics of over-simplified theories and outmoded methodological devices. It is also, in large part, the history of fruitful errors. While the concept of race can be described as both an oversimplified theory and an outmoded methodological approach to the solution of a highly complex problem, it has become these things only for a small number of thinkers, and when the history of the concept of race finally comes to be written, it is unlikely that it will figure prominently, if at all, among the fruitful errors. The probabilities are high that that concept will be afforded a status similar to that now occupied by the nonexistent substance known as "phlogiston." Phlogiston was the substance supposed to be present in all materials and given off by burning. Advanced in the late 17th century by the chemist J. J. Becher, everyone worth his intellectual salt believed in phlogiston as a demonstrable reality, until the true nature of combustion was experimentally demonstrated by Lavoisier a hundred years later. It is an illuminating commentary on the obfuscating effects of erroneous ideas that Joseph Priestley, who stoutly defended the phlogiston theory all his life, was unable to perceive that he had discovered a new gas in 1774, and which according to the false theory he thought to be "dephlogisticated air," but which Lavoisier correctly recognized and named "oxygen."

Race is the phlogiston of our time. During the last two hundred years there have been a number of distinguished critics of the concept of race, Blumenbach, Herder, Thomas Henry Huxley, William Flower, Joseph Deniker, and others. During the 20th century Franz Boas, Lancelot Hogben, Alfred Haddon, and Julian Huxley have been among those who have criticized the validity of this taxonomic category.

As a physical anthropologist I have always found the concept of race unsatisfactory. It was formalistic, artificial, and it arbitrarily circumscribed and defined, without prior or adequate investigation, entities which were declared to be so even before they could possibly be known to be so. I said this, and much more, in a lecture which I delivered at a meeting of the American Association of Physical Anthropologists on 7 April 1941. That lecture was entitled "On the Meaninglessness of the Anthropological Conception of Race," and it is reprinted here, under the title with which it was later published, because it was among the earliest to state clearly and unequivocally what was wrong with the traditional conception of race held by most physical anthropologists—a viewpoint which has been independently developed by most of the contributors to this volume. This paper may serve as an historical introduction to the subject.

In spite of long entrenched beliefs to the contrary, the truth is that there are some things which simply defy all attempts at classification. This is not to say that such things are incapable of systematic study. But it *is* to say that such refractory materials are rendered extremely difficult to investigate in a systematic manner when the attempt is made to force them into the Procrustean bed of some arbitrary classificatory scheme. That, precisely, has been the trouble with the concept of race, for that term and the concept it represents is a classificatory one. It commences with a definition before the inquiry has been undertaken which could render a valid definition possible. Definitions, it should be clear, can only be meaningful at the end of an inquiry rather than at the beginning of one. When one begins with definitions, instead of arriving at them by basing them on the solid and verifiable results of investigation, facts tend to be perceived and ordered according to the requirements of the definitions. Facts, in such a case, tend to be forced to fit the theories which are implied in the definitions. The danger of such theoretical definitions lies in the probability that they will render one insensible to the facts. This, indeed, is exactly what has occurred in connection with the study of the variability which characterizes the human species. There are obvious differences between different human groups, the human species is one, therefore the different human groups must be races; thus the syllogism runs. What is wrong with this syllogism is that the conclusion begs the question implied in the major premise. But this is an oversight that has troubled very few.

Medieval thinkers and scholastics, following Aristotle, attempted to separate things into their generic, specific, essential properties, and accidental ones. The herbalists of the period busily engaged themselves in the useful task of classifying herbs and plants for medicinal purposes, thus leading to our earliest pharmacopoeias. Following their example, Linnaeus, a botanist, applied this method of classification to the whole of animated nature in his *Systema Naturae*, published in 1735, and in a more extended form in the tenth edition of 1758. In this latter edition of his great work, Linnaeus first applied the binomial system of nomenclature to the whole animal kingdom. In this system each species is assigned two names, the first, always printed with an initial capital, indicating the Genus, and the second, printed in lower case, designating the species, both terms are printed in italics. Linnaeus invented neither the concept of Genus nor that of species, but merely adapted them first in 1735 to the systematic ordering of plants, and second, in 1758, to the systematic ordering of animals. It was an invaluable contribution, and enabled men for the first time to classify the whole of animated nature in a systematic manner.

For categories lower than the species the concept of race had already long been available, so that botanists and zoologists, using the Linnaean system, were soon zealously employed in classifying every organic form they could lay their hands on, and reducing it to its lowest common denominator, the subspecies or race. Such taxonomic enthusiasm led in some cases to manifest absurdities, for example, skulls of the two

sexes of the same species, were classified as belonging to different races and in some cases to different species! It need not be
added that the great variety presented by man was not exempt
from the consequences of this taxonomic ardor, and that deep-
seated emotional factors were involved as well as more overtly
conscious ones. It is too often forgotten that taxonomists are
human, that is, not unlike other men, and that in them, as in
other men, motivation and reason are frequently no more
than the obverse and the reverse of the same thing. In an age
of nationalist and imperialist expansion national pride played
no small part in the naming and classification of fossil as well
as of living forms of men. If the concept of race had not
existed it would have had to be invented during this period.
There were reasons for recognizing differences of a biological
nature between human groups. Hence, the concentration on
differences and their description became the principal occupation of the classifier of the races he was only too convinced
were awaiting recognition and discrimination.

First, the races were assumed to exist. Second, they were
recognized. Third, they were described, and fourth, they were
systematically classified. If anything could have been more
arbitrary than this it would be difficult to name it. Yet to this
day there are some anthropologists who believe that this is a
defensible procedure. The present volume is designed to show
why it is not.

In the study of the origin and causes of the variety of man
it is highly undesirable to commence with preconceived ideas
as to the causes or the meaning of the effects. These are the
things we want to discover. It is the height of folly to think
that we know the answers even before we have begun the
inquiry, and yet this is the absurdity to which the very term
race commits us. Dr. Loring Brace, in his contribution, gives
us a fascinating account of the manner in which man's variability is best approached, and, in the light of the verifiable
facts, by discussing the mechanisms which have probably been

involved in the production of that variability, shows us how useful the inductive method can be when applied to such difficult materials, and how useless a rationalization—for that is what it is—a concept like race is when dealing with that material. This is impressively underscored in Dr. Jean Hiernaux' penetrating examination of the concept of race as a classificatory device. Dr. Hiernaux is one of the few investigators who has actually tested the applicability of the concept of race in the field. He has found it utterly useless, unreal, and obfuscating, and says so unequivocally and convincingly.

The formalism which has characterized the physical anthropological preoccupation with race, resulted in the establishment of such scientific myths as the "Armenoid race," on the basis of the fact that this people was supposed to be characterized by a steep back of the head or occiput. Armenoids do have a steep occiput when they are cradled as infants on a cradling board, but not otherwise. When this was demonstrated the "Armenoid race" fell from taxonomic grace and is heard of no more. But an even worse case than this, illustrating the extreme formalism into which the taxonomy of race had fallen, is the traditional classification of the Lapps. This is an extreme case because Lapps look anything but Mongoloid, nevertheless, the observation of a few individuals was sufficient to cause the Lapps to be classified for almost two centuries into our own day as Mongoloids! Dr. Robert T. Anderson deals with this remarkable myth most interestingly. Who first started this hare it is difficult to say, but it appears to have been Blumenbach who put it into print on the basis of some fancied resemblance of Lapp crania to those of Mongoloids. This story of Lappology should serve the reader as a cautionary tale, protecting him against such intuitive physical anthropology as is still practiced by some at the present time, and to which Dr. Anderson makes several illuminating references.

The nature of the variability which physical anthropologists and population geneticists have traditionally attempted to capture and imprison within the framework of the concept of race is such that it has resisted their most strenuous efforts. That variation is continuous, not discontinuous, so that whatever populations are considered they are always found to grade gradually into or incline toward others. Such character gradients are called *clines*. Dr. Frank B. Livingstone discusses the significance of such clinal phenomena in his stimulating contribution on the nonexistence of human races. In common with most of the other contributors to this volume, Dr. Livingstone finds nothing in the human species that corresponds to anything resembling the arbitrary concept of race, and squarely joins the issue with those who do. Dr. Livingstone has already made a few bearded lions roar in their dens. But that is no part of his intention. He is interested in what the variability of the human species is, and not in what anyone thinks it ought to be thought to be. What Dr. Livingstone so well says in this contribution is essentially what I tried, less successfully, to say in my paper of 1941 (pp. 2–11).

The kind of research that Dr. Livingstone has been doing with such notable success, the study of the relation between ecologic factors and genetic change, has an eloquent advocate in Dr. Lancelot Hogben, whose own researches have been fundamental. Dr. Hogben, in the course of the years, has produced some of the most brilliantly persuasive criticisms ever written of race, racism, and what physical anthropologists have been doing. These critical studies have quietly done their work and exerted an important influence upon many of the younger men who have entered the field of physical anthropology. They would agree that Dr. Hogben's parting shot in his contribution applies to the older physical anthropologists, but not to the younger!

If biologists wandered for too long, as Dr. Hogben says, in a barren wilderness of phylogenetic speculation, it should be added that physical anthropologists, until recently, lived in a veritable desert of ideas buried under sandstorms of osteological measurements produced by their own desiccation of what would otherwise have been a rich and fertile terrain. The rich promise of the ecological approach is cogently discussed, as is so much else of relevance to our theme, in Dr. Hogben's stimulating paper.

Some of the confusions current in biological and anthropological thought are illuminatingly discussed by Dr. Nigel Barnicot. Particular attention is drawn to the erroneous paralleling of racial and genetic differences, and the dangers of typological thinking to which the idea of race as a discrete unit characterized by a particular complex of physical attributes, leads. Identical points are made by Drs. Paul Ehrlich and Richard Holm. Indeed, one of the remarkable outcomes of this volume is the unanimity of the views independently arrived at by its contributors. This is very gratifying, and indicates the direction in which future developments may be looked for.

Since the concept of race and the origin of the so-called human races has been the subject of a recent book, which has attracted wide attention, it has been considered desirable to devote some attention to that work, Dr. Carleton S. Coon's *The Origin of Races*, in the present volume. I have therefore included a criticism of that work by myself, not because that critique is superior to others which have appeared, but because it covers some important points which have not been dealt with by other critics.

Dr. Sherwood L. Washburn's contribution provides a fitting conclusion to the volume as a whole, and it remains but to thank the contributors for their ready cooperation in making the present work possible. I should also like to thank Mr. Emanuel Geltman of the Free Press of Glencoe for his sympathetic interest in this book.

Ashley Montagu
PRINCETON, NEW JERSEY

I The Concept of Race in the Human Species in the Light of Genetics

ASHLEY MONTAGU

It is said that when the theory of evolution was first announced it was received by the wife of the Canon of Worcester Cathedral with the remark, "Descended from the apes! My dear, we will hope it is not true. But if it is, let us pray that it may not become generally known."

I rather feel that the attempt to deprive the anthropologist of his belief in race is a piece of cruelty akin to that which sought to deprive the Canon's wife of her belief in special creation. Indeed, the anthropological conception of race and the belief in special creation have much in common. The prevailing attitude of mind is illustrated by the remark of a colleague who, when I gave him an account of this paper replied, somewhat like the Canon's wife, "My dear, I always thought that there was such a thing as race." I believe he had spoken more correctly had he said that he had always taken the idea for granted. Certainly, I had always taken the idea for granted,

Presented originally as a lecture, "The Meaninglessness of the Anthropological Conception of Race," before the American Association of Physical Anthropologists, Chicago, April, 1941, and originally published in *The Journal of Heredity*, Vol. 23, 1941, pp. 243–247. Reprinted from Montagu, *Race, Science, and Humanity*, Princeton, 1963, pp. 1–10, Van Nostrand Co.

and I think all of us have done so. Indeed, the idea of race is
one of the most fundamental. if not *the* most fundamental of
the concepts with which the anthropologist has habitually
worked. To question the validity of this fundamental concept
upon which we were intellectually brought up as if it were an
axiom, was something which simply never occurred to one.
One doesn't question the axioms upon which one's science,
and one's activity in it, are based—at least, not usually. One
simply takes them for granted.

But in science, as in life, it is a good practice, from time to
time, to hang a question mark on the things one takes most for
granted. In science such questioning is important because
without it there is a very real danger that certain erroneous
or arbitrary ideas which may originally have been used merely
as a convenience, may become so fortified by technicality and
so dignified by time that their original infirmities may be
wholly concealed.

Blumenbach, in 1775 and in later years, foresaw this danger with respect to the usage of the term "race," and warned
that it was merely to be used as a convenience helpful to the
memory and no more. Herder, who was the first philosopher
to make extensive use of Blumenbach's work wrote, in 1784
in his *Ideen zur Philosophie Der Geschichte der Menschheit,*
"I could wish the distinctions between the human species, that
have been made from a laudable zeal for discriminating science, not carried beyond the due bounds. Some for instance
have thought fit, to employ the term *races* for four or five
divisions, originally made in consequence of country or complexion: but I see no reason for this appellation. Race refers
to a difference of origin, which in this case does not exist, or
in each of those countries, and under each of these complexions, comprises the most different races. . . . In short, there
are neither four or five races, nor exclusive varieties, on this
Earth. Complexions run into each other: forms follow the

genetic character: and upon the whole, all are at last but shades of the same great picture, extending through all ages, and over all parts of the Earth. They belong not, therefore, so properly to systematic natural history, as to the physicogeographical history of man." When the last word has come to be said upon this subject it will, I am convinced, be very much in the words of Blumenbach and Herder. Meanwhile I propose to make a step in this direction here by showing that the concept of race is nothing but a whited sepulchre, a conception which in the light of modern experimental genetics is utterly erroneous and meaningless, and that it should therefore be dropped from the vocabulary of the anthropologist, for it has done an infinite amount of harm and no good at all.

The development of the idea of race may be clearly traced from the scholastic naturalization of Aristotle's doctrine of the Predicables of Genus, Species, Difference, Property and Accident. From thence it may be directly traced to the early days of the Age of Enlightenment when Linnaeus, in 1735, took over the concepts of Class, Species and Genus from the theologians to serve him as systematic tools. The term race was actually first introduced into the literature of Natural History by Buffon who, in the year 1749, used it to describe six groups of man.

The term merely represented an extension of the Aristotelian conception of Species, that is to say, it was a subdivision of a species. Buffon recognized that all human beings belonged to a single species, as did Linnaeus, and he considered it merely *convenient*, and I emphasize the word convenient, as did Blumenbach after him, to distinguish between certain geographic groups of man. Thus, at the very outset the term was understood to be purely arbitrary and a simple convenience.

The Aristotelian conception of Species, the theological doctrine of special creation and the Natural History of the

Age of Enlightenment, as represented particularly by Cuvier's brilliant conception of Unity of Type, namely the idea that animals can be grouped and classified upon the basis of assemblages of structural characters which, more or less, they have in common, these three conceptions fitted together extremely well and together yielded the idea of the Fixity of Species. An idea which, in spite of every indication to the contrary in the years which followed, was gradually extended to the concept of race.

The Darwinian contribution was to show that species were not as fixed as was formerly believed, and that under the action of Natural Selection one species might give rise to another, that all animal forms might change in this way. It is, however, important to remember that Darwin conceived of evolution as a process involving continuous materials which, without the operation of Natural Selection, would remain unchanged. Hence under the Darwinian conception of species it was still possible to think of species as relatively fixed and immutable, with the modification that under the slow action of Natural Selection they were capable of change. For the nineteenth century anthropologist, therefore, it was possible to think of race, not as Buffon or Blumenbach did in the eighteenth century as an arbitrary convenience in classification, but as Cuvier at the beginning of the nineteenth century had done for all animals, as groups which could be classified upon the basis of the fact that they possessed an aggregate of common physical characters, and as Darwin later postulated, as groups which varied only under the conditions of Natural Selection, but which otherwise remained unchanged.

This is essentially a scholastic conception of species with the one additive fundamental difference that a species is considered to be no longer fixed and immutable. As far as the anthropological conception of race is concerned, the anthropologist who can afford to pass by the findings of experimental genetics, still thinks of race as the scholastics thought of species, as a knowable fixed whole the essence of which could be defined *per genus, species, propria et accidens.*

In fact, what the anthropologist has done has been to take a very crude eighteenth century notion which was originally offered as no more than an arbitrary convenience, and having erected a tremendous terminology and methodology about it, has deceived himself in the belief that he was dealing with an objective reality.

For nearly two centuries anthropologists have been directing their attention principally toward the task of establishing criteria by whose means races of mankind might be defined. All have taken completely for granted the one thing which required to be proven, namely, that the concept of race corresponded with a reality which could actually be measured and verified and descriptively set out so that it could be seen to be a fact. In short, that the anthropological conception of race is true which states that there exists in nature groups of human beings comprised of individuals each of whom possesses a certain aggregate of characters which individually and collectively serve to distinguish them from the individuals in all other groups.

Stated in plain English this is the conception of race which most anthropologists have held and which practically everyone else, except the geneticist, accepts. When, as in recent years, some anthropologists have admitted that the concept cannot be strictly applied in any systematic sense, they have thought to escape the consequences of that fact by calling the term a "general" one, and have proceeded to play the old game of blind man's buff with a sublimity which is almost enviable. For it is not vouchsafed to everyone to appreciate in its full grandeur the doctrine here implied. The feeling of dissatisfaction with which most anthropologists have viewed the many laborious attempts at classification of human races has not, on the whole, succeeded in engendering the disloyal suspicion that something was probably wrong somewhere. If there was a fault, it was generally supposed, it lay not with the anthropologist but with the material, with the human beings themselves who were the subject of classification and who always varied so much that it was difficult to put them into the group where they were conceived to belong, and this was definitely a nuisance, but happily one which could be overcome by the simple expedient of "averaging"—the principal task of the student of "race."

The process of averaging the characters of a given group, knocking the individuals together, giving them a good stirring, and then serving the resulting omelet as a "race" is essentially the anthropological process of race-making. It may be good cooking but it is not science, since it serves to confuse rather than to clarify. When an omelet is done it has a fairly uniform character, though the ingredients which have gone into its making may have been variable. This is what the anthropological conception of "race" is. It is an omelet which corresponds to nothing in nature. It is an indigestible dish conjured into being by an anthropological chef from a number of ingredients which are extremely variable in the characters which they present. The omelet called "race" has no existence outside the statistical frying-pan in which it has been reduced by the heat of the anthropological imagination.

It is this omelet conception of "race" which is so meaningless—meaningless because it is inapplicable to anything real. When anthropologists begin to realize that the proper description of a group does not consist in the process of making an omelet of it, but in the description of the character of the variability of the elements comprising it, its ingredients, they will discover that the fault lies not with the materials but with the conceptual tool with which they have approached its study.

That many differences exist between different groups of human beings is obvious, but the anthropological conception of these is erroneous, and the anthropological approach to the study of their relationships is unscientific and pre-Mendelian. Taxonomic exercises in the classification of assemblages of phenotypical characters will never succeed in elucidating the relationships of different groups of mankind to one another for the simple reason that it is not assemblages of characters which undergo change in the formation of the individual and of the group, but single units which influence the development of those characters. One of the great persisting errors involved in the anthropological conception of race has been due to the steady refusal to recognize this fact. The fact that it is not possible to classify the various groups of mankind by means of the characters which anthropologists customarily use, because these characters do not behave as pre-Mendelian, anthropologists think that they should behave, namely, as complexes of characters which are relatively fixed and are transmitted as complexes. Those characters instead behave in a totally different manner as the expressions of many independent units which have entered into their formation.

The materials of evolution are not represented by continuous aggregates which in turn determine particular aggregates of characters, but by discontinuous packages of chemicals, each of which is independent in its action and may be only partially responsible for the ultimate form of any character. These chemical packages are the genes, with which most anthropologists are still scarcely on terms of a bowing acquaintance. These genes retain both their independence and their individual character more or less indefinitely, although they are probably all inherently variable and, in time, capable of mutation. For these reasons any conception of race which operates as if inheritance were a matter of the transmission of gross aggregates of character is meaningless.

The principal agencies of evolutionary change in man are primarily gene variability and gene mutation, that is to say, through the rearrangement of gene combinations in consequence of the operation of many secondary factors, physical and social, and change in the character of genes themselves. In order to appreciate the meaning of the variety presented by mankind today it is indispensably necessary to understand the manner in which these agencies work. Thus, in man, it is practically certain that some forms of hair, and skin color, are due to mutation, while still other forms are due to various combinations of these mutant forms with one another as also with nonmutant forms. The rate of mutation for different genes in man is unknown, though it has been calculated that the gene for normal clotting mutates, for example, to the gene for hemophilia in one out of every 50,000 individuals per generation. It is highly probable, for example, that such a mutation occurred in the person of Queen Victoria's father, a fact which in the long run may perhaps prove her chief claim to fame. Mutation of the blood group genes is, however known to be very slow. Mutation of skin color genes is also very slow, while mutation of hair form genes is relatively frequent.

If we are ever to understand how the differing groups of mankind came to possess such characters as distinguish the more geographically isolated of them, and those of the less isolated more recently mixed, and therefore less distinguishable, groups, it should be obvious that we shall never succeed in doing so if we make omelets of the very ingredients, the genes, which it should be our purpose to isolate and map. We must study the frequencies with which such genes occur in different groups. If, roughly speaking, we assign one gene to every component of the human body it should be fairly clear that as regards the structure of man we are dealing with many thousands of genes. If we consider the newer genetic concepts which recognize that the adult individual represents the end-point in an interaction between all these genes, the complexities become even greater. The morphological characters which anthropologists have relied upon for their "racial" classifications have been very few indeed, involving a minute fraction of the great number of genes which it would actually be necessary to consider in attempting to make any real, that is to say, genetically analytic, classification of mankind.

To sum up, the indictment against the anthropological conception of race is (1) that it is artificial; (2) that it does not agree with the facts; (3) that it leads to confusion and the perpetuation of error, and finally, that for all these reasons it is meaningless, or rather more accurately such meaning as it possesses is false. Being so weighed down with false meaning it were better that the term were dropped altogether than that any attempt should be made to give it a new meaning.

If it be agreed that the human species is one and that it consists of a group of populations which, more or less, replace each other geographically or ecologically and of which the neighboring ones intergrade or hybridize wherever they are in contact, or are potentially capable of doing so, then it should be obvious that the task of the student interested in the character of these populations must lie in the study of the frequency distribution of the genes which characterize them— and not in the study of entities which have no meaning.

In conclusion, let me say that I realize how unsatisfactory this paper is, and that I cannot expect to have convinced you, in these few pages, of the meaninglessness of the anthropological concept of race. It may be that a notion so many times attacked during recent years is now passed beyond the reach both of scientific judgment and mortal malice, but in any event, may I be so bold as to hope that you will not feel as the Canon's wife felt about the threat to her belief in special creation?

This article was the subject of an unusual and gratifying procedure. The editor of the Journal of Heredity, *Dr. Robert C. Cook, considered it important enough to append to it the following editorial comments, which because of their interest are reprinted here.*

Dr. Ashley Montagu's interesting history of the term race, shows certain ways it has outgrown any usefulness, even becoming a menace. Some of his views may draw fire from geneticists, for humankind differs greatly in many characteristics variously distributed. If these differences are real enough to allow objective groupings of people, such groups will differ just as much whether we call them "races" or invent a new term. If Dr. Montagu's idol smashing helps to clear the air it has served a very useful purpose.

The laboratory scientist shuns the market place and the politician's rostrum. Unfortunately folks accustomed to reach for a microphone refuse to stay out of the laboratory if they see a chance to gain even reluctant support for their pet nostrum. Because "race" is a word which inflames the emotions, much fanatical nonsense has been spoken and written about it. "Class" is another word called upon to carry an impossible genetic load, as the history of the eugenics movement testifies. Strange perversions, allegedly sanctioned by careful laboratory research, perplex and enslave millions of people.

Research workers in those sciences which may become social dynamite through perversion or prostitution of conclusions, may have to defend the integrity of their science whether they like it or not. This is emphasized in the depths of biological absurdity recently reached by champions of "racism" (a derivative word with very ugly connotations). Even the Norwegians have been read out of the Aryan fold by the dark-moustached "protector" of destiny-freighted blonds. The color of Norwegian hair and eyes has not changed. Rugged Norse individualism has made it impossible for the most "nordic" group in the world to accept the Procrustean savagery of the "new order."

With racism thus divorced by its leading proponent from

shape of head and color of hair, eyes, and skin, it is essential that anthropologists and biologists clarify their own minds and inform lay people what actually are the differences between the human races. The study of human relationships through an analysis of gene distributions is as yet limited mainly to the blood groups and to P.T.C. taste reaction. The technique offers a hopeful approach which needs to be further explored.

As far as research and observation have been able to prove, the chromosome number of all the human races is the same, and all of the five, seven, or ten races (depending on who we follow) are inter-fertile. The blood of all races is built of the same pattern of agglutinins and antigens, and the appropriate blood type from one race can be transfused into any of the others without untoward effect. Thus in spite of the unquestionable physical differences (and less measurable mental and emotional differences) between groups of people, an imposing substrate of similarity underlies these differences. This must serve as a foundation for a world order willing to accept the differences as a challenge to developing useful specializations and not as a fatuous excuse for the enslavement or exploitation of one "race," class or nation by another.

II   The Concept of Race

ASHLEY MONTAGU

In this paper I desire to examine the concepts of a race as they are used with reference to man. I shall first deal with the use of this term by biologists and anthropologists, and then with its use by the man-on-the-street, the so-called layman—so-called, no doubt, from the lines in Sir Philip Sidney's sonnet:

> I never drank of Aganippe well
> Nor ever did in shade of Tempe sit,
> And Muses scorn with vulgar brains to dwell;
> Poor layman I, for sacred rites unfit.

I shall endeavor to show that all those who continue to use the term "race" with reference to man, whether they be laymen or scientists, are "for sacred rites unfit." Once more, I shall, as irritatingly as the sound of a clanging door heard in the distance in a wind that will not be shut out, raise the question as to whether, with reference to man, it would not be better if the term "race" were altogether abandoned.

At the outset it should, perhaps, be made clear that I be-

Presented at the University Seminar on Genetics and the Evolution of Man, Columbia University, December 6, 1959. Reprinted from *American Anthropologist*, Vol. 64, No. 5, Part I, October, 1962.

lieve, with most biologists, that evolutionary factors, similar
to those that have been operative in producing raciation in
other animal species, have also been operative in the human
species—but with a significant added difference, namely, the
consequences which have resulted from man's entry into that
unique zone of adaptation in which he excels beyond all other
creatures, namely *culture*, that is to say, the man-made part
of the environment.

On the evidence it would seem clear that man's cultural
activities have introduced elements into the processes of human evolution which have so substantially modified the end-
products that one can no longer equate the processes of
raciation in lower animals with the related processes which
have occurred in the evolution of man. The factors of mutation, natural selection, drift, isolation, have all been operative
in the evolution of man. But so have such factors as ever-
increasing degrees of mobility, hybridization, and social selection, and it is the effects of these and similar factors which, at
least so it has always seemed to me, makes the employment of
the term "race" inapplicable to most human populations as we
find them today.

Of course there exist differences, but we want a term by
which to describe the existence of these differences. We do
not want a prejudiced term which injects meanings which are
not there into the differences. We want a term which as
nearly mirrors the conditions as a term can, not one which
falsifies and obfuscates the issue.

Terminology is extremely important, and I think it will
be generally agreed that it is rather more desirable to allow the
conditions or facts to determine the meaning of the terms by
which we shall refer to them, than to have pre-existing terms
determine the manner in which they shall be perceived and
ordered, for pre-existing terms constitute pre-existing meanings, and such meanings have a way of conditioning the man-

ner in which what we look at shall be perceived. Each time
the term "race" is used with reference to man, this is what,
I think, is done.

The term "race" has a long and tortured history. We cannot enter upon that here. The present-day usage of the term
in biological circles is pretty much the sense in which it was
used in similar circles in the 19th century, namely, as a subdivision of a species the members of which resemble each
other and differ from other members of the species in certain
traits. In our own time valiant attempts have been made to
pour new wine into the old bottles. The shape of the bottle,
however, remains the same. The man-on-the-street uses the
term in much the same way as it was used by his 19th century
compeer. Here physical type, heredity, blood, culture, nation,
personality, intelligence, and achievement are all stirred together to make the omelet which is the popular conception of
"race." This is a particularly virulent term, the epidemiology
of which is far better understood by the social scientist than
by the biologist—who should, therefore, exercise somewhat
more restraint and rather more caution than he usually does
when he delivers himself on the subject.

The difficulty with taking over old terms in working with
problems to which they are thought to apply is that when
this is done we may also take over some of the old limitations
of the term, and this may affect our approach to the solution
of these problems. For what the investigator calls "the problem
of human races" is immediately circumscribed and delimited
the moment he uses the word "races." For "race" implies
something very definite to him, something which in itself constitutes a solution, and the point I would like to make is that
far from the problem meaning something like a solution to
him, it should, on the contrary, constitute itself in his mind
as something more closely resembling what it is, namely, a
problem requiring investigation.

Instead of saying to himself, as the true believer in "race" does, "Here is a population, let me see how it fits my criteria of 'race,'" I think it would be much more fruitful of results if he said to himself, instead, "Here is a population, let me go ahead and find out what it is like. What its internal likenesses and differences are, and how it resembles and how it differs from other populations. And then let me operationally describe what I have found," that is, in terms of the data themselves, and not with reference to the conditions demanded by any pre-existing term.

The chief objection to the term "race" with reference to man is that it takes for granted as solved problems which are far from being so and tends to close the mind to problems to which it should always remain open. If, with ritual fidelity, one goes on repeating long enough that "the Nordics" are a race, or that "the Armenoids" are, or that "the Jews" are, or that races may be determined by their blood group gene frequencies, we have already determined what a "race" is, and it is not going to make the slightest difference whether one uses the old or the new wine, for we are back at the same old stand pouring it into the old bottles covered with the same patina of moss-like green.

It is the avoidance of this difficulty that T. H. Huxley had in mind when in 1865, he wrote, "I speak of 'persistent modifications' or 'stocks' rather than of 'varieties,' or 'races,' or 'species,' because each of these last well-known terms implies, on the part of its employer, a preconceived opinion touching one of those problems, the solution of which is the ultimate object of the science; and in regard to which, therefore, ethnologists are especially bound to keep their minds open and their judgements freely balanced" (1895:209–10).

It is something to reflect upon that, a century later, this point of view has still to be urged.

In the year 1900, the French anthropologist Joseph Deniker published his great book, simultaneously in French and in English, *The Races of Man*. But though the title has the word in it, he objected to the term "race" on much the same grounds as Huxley. The whole of his introduction is devoted to showing the difficulties involved in applying to man the terms of zoological nomenclature. He writes, "We have presented to us Arabs, Swiss, Australians, Bushmen, English, Siouan Indians, Negroes, etc., without knowing if each of these groups is on an equal footing from the point of view of classification."

Do these real and palpable groupings represent unions of individuals which, in spite of some slight dissimilarities, are capable of forming what zoologists call "species," "subspecies," "varieties," in the case of wild animals, or "races" in the case of domestic animals? One need not be a professional anthropologist to reply negatively to this question. They are *ethnic groups* formed by virtue of community of language, religion, social institutions, etc., which have the power of uniting human beings of one or several species, races, or varieties, and are by no means zoological species; they may include human beings of one or of many species, races, or varieties. They are [he goes on to say] theoretic types (1900:2–3).

Writing in 1936 Franz Boas remarked "We talk all the time glibly of races and nobody can give us a definite answer to the question what constitutes a race." And recollecting his early days as a physical anthropologist Boas comments, "When I turned to the consideration of racial problems I was shocked by the formalism of the work. Nobody had tried to answer the questions why certain measurements were taken, why they were considered significant, whether they were subject to other influences." (1936:140).

When, in the same year, 1936, Julian Huxley and A. C. Haddon published their valuable book on "race," *We Europeans*, they took pains to underscore the fact that "the existence of . . . human sub-species is purely hypothetical. Nowhere does a human group now exist which corresponds

closely to a systematic sub-species in animals, since various
original sub-species have crossed repeatedly and constantly.
For the existing populations, the non-committal term *ethnic
group* should be used. . . . All that exists today is a number of
arbitrary ethnic groups, intergrading into each other" (1936:
106). And finally, "The essential reality of the existing situation . . . is not the hypothetical sub-species or races, but the
mixed ethnic groups, which can never be genetically purified
into their original components, or purged of the variability
which they owe to past crossing. Most anthropological writings of the past, and many of the present fail to take account
of this fundamental fact" (1936:108). "If *race* is a scientific
term," these authors point out, "it must have a genetic meaning" (1936:114).

Haddon, as an anthropologist, was familiar with Deniker's
book, and it is possible that the noncommittal term "ethnic
group" was remembered by him as one more appropriately
meeting the requirements of the situation and thus came to be
adopted by both authors in their book. It was from this source,
that is from Huxley and Haddon, that I, in turn, adopted the
term "ethnic group" in 1936 and have consistently continued
to use it since that time. The claim is that the noncommittal
general term "ethnic group" meets the realities of the situation
head on, whereas the term "race" does not. Furthermore, it is
claimed that "ethnic group" is a term of heuristic value. It
raises questions, and doubts, leading to clarification and discovery. The term "race," since it takes for granted what requires to be demonstrated within its own limits, closes the
mind on all that.

It is of interest to find that quite a number of biologists
have, in recent years, independently raised objections to the
continuing use of the term "race," even, in some cases, when
it is applied to populations of lower animals. Thus, for example, W. T. Calman writes, "Terms such as 'geographical

race,' 'form,' 'phase,' and so forth, may be useful in particular
instances but are better not used until some measure of agreement is reached as to their precise meaning" (1949:14). Hans
Kalmus writes, "A very important term which was originally
used in systematics is 'race.' Nowadays, however, its use is
avoided as far as possible in genetics" (1948:45). In a later
work Kalmus writes, "It is customary to discuss the local varieties of humanity in terms of 'race.' However, it is unnecessary
to use this greatly debased word, since it is easy to describe
populations without it" (1958:30). G. S. Carter writes that the
terms " 'race,' 'variety,' and 'form' are used so loosely and in
so many senses that it is advisable to avoid using them as infraspecific categories (1951:163). Ernst Hanhart objects to the
use of the term "race" with reference to man since he holds
that there are no "true races" among men (1953:545). Abercrombie, Hickman, and Johnson, in their *A Dictionary of
Biology* (1951), while defining species and subspecies consistently, decline even a mention of the word "race" anywhere
in their book. L. S. Penrose in an otherwise highly favorable
review of Dunn and Dobzhansky's excellent *Heredity, Race
and Society*, writes that he is unable "to see the necessity for
the rather apologetic retention of the obsolete term 'race,'
when what is meant is simply a given population differentiated
by some social, geographical or genetical character, or . . .
merely by a gene frequency peculiarity. The use of the almost
mystical concept of race makes the presentation of the facts
about the geographical and linguistic groups . . . unnecessarily
complicated" (1952:252).

To see what Penrose means, and at the same time to make
our criticism of their conception of "race," let us turn to Dunn
and Dobzhansky's definition of race. They write, in the aforementioned work, "Races can be defined as populations which
differ in the frequencies of some gene or genes" (1952:118).
This definition at once leads to the question: Why use the

word "race" here when what is being done is precisely what should be done, namely, to describe populations in terms of their gene frequency differences? What, in point of fact, has the antiquated, mystical conception of "race" to do with this? The answer is: Nothing. Indeed, the very notion of "race" is antithetical to the study of population genetics, for the former traditionally deals with fixed clear-cut differences, and the latter with fluid or fluctuating differences. It seems to me an unrealistic procedure to maintain this late in the day that we can readapt the term "race" to mean something utterly different from what it has always most obfuscatingly and ambiguously meant.

We may congratulate ourselves and in fact often do, that the chemists of the late 18th and early 19th centuries had the good sense to throw out the term "phlogiston" when they discovered that it corresponded to nothing in reality, instead of attempting to adapt it to fit the facts which it was not designed to describe, and of which, indeed, it impeded the discovery for a hundred years. The psychologists of the second decade of this century had the good sense to do likewise with the term "instinct" when they discovered how, like a bunion upon the foot, it impeded the pilgrim's progress toward a sounder understanding of human drives (Bernard 1924).

It is a hopeless task to attempt to redefine words with so longstanding a history of misuse as "race," and for this, among other cogent reasons, it is ill-advised. As Simpson has said, "There . . . is a sort of Gresham's Law for words; redefine them as we will, their worst or most extreme meaning is almost certain to remain current and to tend to drive out the meaning we prefer" (1953:268).

For this reason alone it would appear to me unwise to afford scientific sanction to a term which is so embarrassed by false meanings as is the term "race." There is the added objection that it is wholly redundant, and confusingly so, to distinguish as a "race" a population which happens to differ from other populations in the frequency of one or more genes. Why call such populations "races" when the operational definition of what they *are* is sharply and clearly stated in the words used to convey what we mean, namely, populations which differ from one another in particular frequencies of certain specified genes? Surely, to continue the use of the word "race" under such circumstances is to exemplify what A. E. Housman so aptly described as "calling in ambiguity of language to promote confusion of thought" (1933:31).

When populations differ from each other in the frequency of sickle-cell gene or any other gene or genes, all that is necessary is to state the facts with reference to those populations. That is what those populations are in terms of gene frequencies. And those are the operative criteria which we can use as tools or concepts in giving an account of the realities of the situation—the actual operations.

I have thus far said nothing about the anthropological conception of "race" because this is to some extent yielding to genetic pressure, and because the future of what used to be called the study of "race" lies, in my view, largely in the direction of population genetics. The older anthropological conception of "race" still lingers on, suggesting that it is perhaps beyond the reach both of scientific judgment and mortal malice. Insofar as the genetic approach to the subject is concerned, many anthropologists are, as it were, self-made men and only too obviously represent cases of unskilled labor. However, my feeling is that they should be praised for trying rather than blamed for failing. The new anthropology is on the right track.

Recently Garn and Coon (1955) have attempted to adapt the terms "geographic race," "local race," and "microgeographical race," for use in the human species. They define, for example, "A geographical race" as, "in its simplest terms, a collection of (race) populations having features in common, such as a high gene frequency for blood group B, and extending over a geographically definable area" (1955:997).

In this definition I think we can see, in high relief as it were, what is wrong with the continuing use of the term "race." The term "geographical race" immediately delimits the group of populations embraced by it from others, as if the so-called "geographical race" were a biological entity "racially" distinct from others. Such a group of populations is not "racially" distinct, but differs from others in the frequencies of certain of its genes. It was suggested by the UNESCO group of geneticists and physical anthropologists that such a group of populations be called a "major group" (Montagu 1951:173–82). This suggestion was made precisely in order to avoid such difficulties as are inherent in the term "geographical race." Since Garn and Coon themselves admit that "geographical races are to a large extent collections of convenience, useful more for pedagogic purposes than as units for empirical investigation" (1955:1000), it seems to me difficult to understand why they should have preferred this term to the one more closely fitting the situation, namely, "major groups." It is a real question whether spurious precision, even for pedagogical purposes, or as an "as if" fiction, is to be preferred to a frank acknowledgment, in the terms we use, of the difficulties involved. Garn and Coon are quite alive to the problem, but it may be questioned whether it contributes to the student's clearer understanding of that problem to use terms which not only do not fit the conditions, but which serve to contribute to making the student's mind a dependable instrument of imprecision, especially in view of the fact that a more appropriate term is available.

The principle of "squatter's rights" apparently applies to words as well as to property. When men make a heavy investment in words they are inclined to treat them as property, and even to become enslaved by them, the prisoners of their own vocabularies. High walls may not a prison make, but technical terms sometimes do. This, I would suggest, is another good reason for self-examination with regard to the use of the term "race."

Commenting of Garn's views on race, Dr. J. P. Garlick has remarked,

The use of "race" as a taxonomic unit for man seems out of date, if not irrational. A hierarchy of geographical, local and micro-races is proposed, with acknowledgments to Rensch and Dob-zhansky. But the criteria for their definition are nowhere made clear, and in any case such a scheme could not do justice to the many independent fluctuations and frequency gradients shown by human polymorphic characters. Surely physical anthropology has outgrown such abstractions as "Large Local Race. . . . Alpine: the rounder-bodied, rounder-headed, predominantly darker peoples of the French mountains, across Switzerland, Austria, and to the shores of the Black Sea" (1961:169–70).

Garn and Coon do not define "local races" but say of them that they "can be identified, not so much by average differ-ences, but by their nearly complete isolation" (1955:997). In that case, as Dahlberg (1942) long ago suggested, why not call such populations "isolates"?

"Microgeographical races" also fail to receive definition, but are described as differing "only qualitatively from local races." In that case, why not use some term which suggests the difference?

In short, it is our opinion that taxonomies and terms should be designed to fit the facts, and not the facts forced into the procrustean rack of pre-determined categories. If we are to have references, whether terminological or taxonomical, to ex-isting or extinct populations of man, let the conditions as we find them determine the character of our terms or taxonomies, and not the other way round.

Since what we are actually dealing with in human breeding populations are differences in the frequencies of certain genes, why not use a term which states just this, such as *genogroup*, and the various appropriate variants of this?[1] If necessary, we could then speak of "geographic genogroups," "local genogroups," and "microgenogroups." A genogroup being defined as a breeding population which differs from other breeding populations of the species in the frequency of one or more genes. The term "genogroup" gets as near to a statement of the facts as a term can. The term "race" goes far beyond the facts and only serves to obscure them. A *geographic genogroup* would then be defined as a group of breeding populations characterized by a marked similarity of the frequencies of one or more genes.

A *local genogroup* would be one of the member populations of a geographic genogroup, and a *microgenogroup* a partially isolated population with one or more gene frequency differences serving to distinguish it from adjacent or non-adjacent local genogroups.

It is to be noted that nothing is said of a common heredity for similarity in gene frequencies in a geographic genogroup. The common heredity is usually implied, but I do not think it should be taken for granted, except within the local genogroups and the microgenogroups. One or more of the genogroups in a geographic genogroup may have acquired their frequencies for a given gene quite independently of the other local populations comprising the geographic genogroup. This is a possibility which is, perhaps, too often overlooked when comparisons are being made on the basis of gene frequencies between populations, whether geographic or not.

But this must suffice for my criticism of the usage of the term "race" by biologists and anthropologists. I wish now to

1. The term "genogroup" was suggested to me by Sir Julian Huxley during a conversation on September 29, 1959.

discuss, briefly, the disadvantages of the use of this term in popular usage, and the advantages of the general term "ethnic group."

The layman's conception of "race" is so confused and emotionally muddled that any attempt to modify it would seem to be met by the greatest obstacle of all, the term "race" itself. It is a trigger word. Utter it, and a whole series of emotionally conditioned responses follow. If we are to succeed in clarifying the minds of those who think in terms of "race" we must cease using the word, because by continuing to use it we sanction whatever meaning anyone chooses to bestow upon it, and because in the layman's mind the term refers to conditions which do not apply. There is no such thing as the kind of "race" in which the layman believes, namely, that there exists an indissoluble association between mental and physical characters which make individual members of certain "races" either inferior or superior to the members of certain other "races." The layman requires to have his thinking challenged on this subject. The term "ethnic group" serves as such a challenge to thought and as a stimulus to rethink the foundations of one's beliefs. The term "race" takes for granted what should be a matter for inquiry. And this is precisely the point that is raised when one uses the noncommittal "ethnic group." It encourages the passage from ignorant or confused certainty to thoughtful uncertainty. For the layman, as for others, the term "race" closes the door on understanding. The phrase "ethnic group" opens it, or at the very least, leaves it ajar.

In opposition to these views a number of objections have been expressed. Here are some of them. One does not change anything by changing names. It is an artful dodge. It is a subterfuge. Why not meet the problem head-on? If the term has been badly defined in the past, why not redefine it? Re-education should be attempted by establishing the true meaning of "race," not by denying its existence. It suggests a certain blindness to the facts to deny that "races" exist in man. One cannot combat racism by enclosing the word in quotes. It is not the word that requires changing but people's ideas about it. It is a common failing to argue from the abuse of an idea to its total exclusion. It is quite as possible to feel "ethnic group prejudice" as it is to feel "race prejudice." One is not going to solve the race problem this way.

Such objections indicate that there has been a failure of communication, that the main point has been missed. The term "ethnic group" is not offered as a substitute for "race." On the contrary, the term "ethnic group" implies a fundamental difference in viewpoint from that which is implied in the term "race." It is not a question of changing names or of substitution, or an artful dodge, or the abandonment of a good term which has been abused. It is first and foremost an attempt to clarify the fact that the old term is unsound when applied to man, and should therefore not be used with reference to man. At the same time "ethnic group," being an intentionally vague and general term, is designed to make it clear that there is a problem to be solved, rather than to maintain the fiction that the problem has been solved. As a general term it leaves all question of definition open, referring specifically to human breeding populations, the members of which are believed to exhibit certain physical or genetic likenesses. For all general purposes, an "ethnic group" may be defined as one of a number of breeding populations, which populations together comprise the species *Homo sapiens*, and which individually maintain their differences, physical or genetic and cultural, by means of isolating mechanisms such as geographic and social barriers.

The re-education of the layman should be taken seriously. For this reason I would suggest that those who advocate the redefinition of the term "race," rather than its replacement by a general term which more properly asks questions before it attempts definitions, would do well to acquaint themselves with the nature of the laymen as well as with the meaning of the phenomena to which they would apply a term which cannot possibly be redefined. If one desires to remove a prevailing erroneous conception and introduce a more correct one, one is more likely to be successful by introducing the new conception with a distinctively new term rather than by attempting redefinition of a term embarrassed by longstanding unsound usage. Professor Henry Sigerist has well said that "it is never sound to continue the use of terminology with which the minds of millions of people have been poisoned even when the old terms are given new meanings" (1951:101).

There is, apparently, a failure on the part of some students to understand that one of the greatest obstacles to the process of re-education would be the retention of the old term "race," a term which enshrines the errors it is designed to remove. The deep implicit meanings this term possesses for the majority of its users are such that they require immediate challenge whenever and by whomsoever the term "race" is used.

Whenever the term "race" is used, most people believe that something like an eternal verity has been uttered when, in fact, nothing more than evidence has been given that there are many echoes, but few voices. "Race" is a word so familiar that in using it the uncritical thinker is likely to take his own private meaning for it completely for granted, never thinking at any time to question so basic an instrument of the language as the word "race." On the other hand, when one uses the term "ethnic group," the question is immediately raised, "What does it mean? What does the user have in mind?" And this at once affords an opportunity to discuss the facts and explore the meaning and the falsities enshrined in the word "race," and to explain the problems involved and the facts of the genetic situation as we know them.

The term "ethnic group" is concerned with questions; the

term "race" is concerned with answers, unsound answers, where for the most part there are only problems that require to be solved before any sound answers can be given.

It may be difficult for those who believe in what I. A. Richards has called "The Divine Right of Words" to accept the suggestion that a word such as "race," which has exercised so evil a tyranny over the minds of men, should be permanently dethroned from the vocabulary, but that constitutes all the more reason for trying, remembering that the meaning of a word is the action it produces.

References

Abercrombie, M., C. J. Hickman, and M. L. Johnson. 1951. *A Dictionary of Biology*. Harmondsworth, Penguin Books.

Bernard, L. L., 1924. *Instinct*. New York, Henry Holt and Co.

Boas, F. 1936. History and science in anthropology. *American Anthropologist* 38:140.

Calman, W. T. 1949. *The Classification of Animals*. New York, John Wiley and Sons.

Carter, G. S. 1951. *Animal Evolution*. New York, Columbia University Press.

Dahlberg, G. 1942. *Race, Reason and Rubbish*. New York, Columbia University Press.

Deniker, J. 1900. *The Races of Man*. London, Walter Scott Ltd.

Dunn, L. C. and Th. Dobzhansky. 1952. *Heredity, Race and Society*. Rev. ed. New York, New American Library.

Garlick, J. P. 1961. Review of *Human Races and Readings on Race*, by S. M. Garn. *Annals of Human Genetics* 25:169–70.

Garn, S. M., and C. S. Coon. 1955. On the number of races of mankind. *American Anthropologist* 57:996–1001.

Hanhart, E. 1953. Infectious diseases. In *Clinical Genetics*, Arnold Sorsby, ed. St. Louis, Mosby.

Housman, A. E. 1933. *The Name and Nature of Poetry*. New York, Cambridge University Press.

Huxley, J. S. and A. C. Haddon. 1936. *We Europeans: a survey of "racial" problems.* New York. Harper and Bros.

Huxley, T. H. 1865. On the methods and results of ethnology. *Fortnightly Review.* Reprinted in *Man's Place in Nature and Other Anthropological Essays.* London, Macmillan Co., 1894.

Kalmus, H. 1948. *Genetics.* Harmondsworth, Pelican Books.

————1958. *Heredity and Variation.* London, Routledge and K. Paul.

Montagu, M. F. Ashley. 1951. *Statement on Race.* Rev. ed. New York, Henry Schuman.

Penrose, L. S. 1952. Review of *Heredity, Race and Society*, by Dunn and Dobzhansky. *Annals of Human Eugenics* 17:252.

Sigerist, H. 1951. *A History of Medicine.* Vol. 1. New York, Oxford University Press.

Simpson, G. G. 1953. *The Major Features of Evolution.* New York, Columbia University Press.

III The Concept of Race and the Taxonomy of Mankind

JEAN HIERNAUX

Introduction

Race has been given numerous definitions. Many of them are similar in meaning, but several modes of thinking about race still persist. Within a single mode, the formulation of the concept may differ, and some vagueness in it is frequent. Moreover, application of the concept of race by an author to a classification of mankind does not always meet the requirements of his own definition.

I do not intend to review the literature on race and human races. Only a few contributions will be cited as examples. I shall attempt, where so many others have failed, to reach the most sensible and useful definition, and this as a development of a previous paper on the subject (Hiernaux 1962) presented at the sixth International Congress of Anthropological and Ethnological Sciences, Paris, 1960. Once this definition is arrived at, I shall endeavor to apply it to current mankind, in other words to apply the concept of race to a classification of mankind into races.

Toward a Definition of Race

1. A race is a grouping of persons.

There is common agreement on this point: if every individual belonged to a different race, there would be no need for a concept other than that of the individual. The concept of race is obviously a classificatory one: it tends to reduce the immense number of individuals to a more limited number of classes. As in any classification, a hierarchy of groupings may be conceived, for example, one consisting of three grades called grand race, race, and subrace—or similar terms.

2. What in Man determines race?

Factors of two orders determine the characters of an individual: heredity and environment. In defining race, do we have to consider the genotype only? Or do we have to consider the phenotype, thus including noninherited characters and the nontransmissible influence of the environment?

All concepts of race are interwoven with that of heredity because all aim to define something that has a tendency, at least, to remain stable from one generation to the next. Suppose two groups of people have identical gene pools, but differ phenotypically because of the imprint of different environments. Would it be useful to call them races A and B, knowing that by reversing the environmental conditions race A would become race B in one generation and vice versa? A negative answer seems evident to me as to many others: in order to be useful, a concept of race must be genetical. When using characters known to be partly sensitive to environmental differences, the concept of race is correctly used only when the genetically induced variability is considered. Coon, Garn, and Birdsell (1950), however, write: "A race is a population which differs phenotypically from all others with which it has been compared." The usefulness of such a concept is much less than that of race as a group of individuals characterized by its gene pool.

3. How to group individuals?

Two basic answers have been given to this question. One of them is: let us group together all similar individuals, wherever they live or have lived. Analyzing the various views on race, Vallois (1953) shows how widely this way of grouping has been used until recently: "the notion of race . . . may be understood, first of all, as a combination of characters discernible in individuals." For example, Frankenberg (1956) writes: "Rasse zweierlei bedeutet 1. Einem komplex erblicher merkmale. . . . 2. Eine gruppe von individuen, die diese merkmale zu besitzen pflegen." ("Race has two meanings. 1. A complex of hereditary characteristics. . . . 2. A group of individuals tending to possess these characteristics.") Though adhered to by a much smaller proportion of anthropologists, this concept of race is still alive today. For example, Wierciński (1962) and Czekanowski (1962) plead in its favour and recent studies on the Swiss (Gloor 1961–62) and on the Basques (Marquer 1963) use it. Arguments against the theoretical bases of such a concept of race have been expressed too often to be listed here again; the discussion in *Current Anthropology* of Wierciński's paper sums up most of them. Only one aspect of this concept will be considered here. We know that mankind has evolved and is still physically evolving. The groups of individuals that constitute our taxonomic units must be such as to allow investigation of those evolutionary processes: Those groups must both show a tendency toward secular stability and reflect evolutionary change. But a race defined as a group of similar individuals is, by definition, incapable of any change. In each generation it will consist of an artificial grouping of people who happen to share a given constellation of characters.

To me, as to many others, it seems that the only useful way of grouping individuals for anthropological analysis is to group together the people participating within the same circle of matings. Such a group shows a genuine tendency toward stability from generation to generation. If it is closed, sufficiently large, and not submitted to selection, the filial generations will have the same gene pool as the parental ones. In contrast, the offspring of a "racial type" may belong to many other types, each member of it having been conceived by two persons who may largely differ, as a result of Mendelian segregation. Evolutionary forces and events will act against the tendency toward stability of the group just defined, and a quantitative study of this process is possible.

To delimit in an absolute way the circle of matings to which an individual belongs is feasible only in the rare case of a strictly closed panmictic community, that is, in an isolate. In all other cases, the delineation is only relative. If two panmictic groups exchange mates but their members marry within their own group with a higher frequency, the partly permeable barrier to gene flow delineates them—be it of geographical, political, social, religious, or linguistic nature. But if both are surrounded by other groups with which they exchange genes at a lower rate, a barrier of a higher order includes them both. If the frequency of matings between different localities is mainly an inverse function of distance, then the only boundaries that can be traced around each locality are delimited in terms of percentage of intragroup matings and the circles overlap. The only way to group individuals in a biological sense thus often requires a probabilistic criterion for its application.

Let us ignore this difficulty and suppose that we could assign each individual to a demarcated circle of matings, for which the term "population" will be used here. Will we equate the concept of race with that of breeding population as just defined? Our grouping of individuals in one population did not take into consideration their characters in any way, it made no use of any taxonomic procedure, it was offered only in order to constitute a biological unit of study. If we want to keep the term "race" for taxonomic purposes, it may not be applied to the population. One word is enough for one thing, and a taxonomic class may not be equated with the units to be classified. Race is a much more useful concept if we consider it as a grouping of populations. Numerous authors however equate race and population. For example, Garn (1961) defines a local race as a breeding population and even uses the term "race-population." Dunn and Dobzhansky (1952) write: "Races can be defined as populations which differ in the frequencies of some gene or genes." Howells (1959) finds Dobzhansky's definition: "Races are populations differing in the incidence of certain genes" the most acceptable. These authors also use, explicitly or not, higher taxonomic classes below the human species, for example, Garn uses "geographical race," and at this level they rejoin the concept of race here proposed: a race is a group of populations.

Application of the Concept of Race to a Classification of Mankind

Let us first approach the problem of a taxonomic subdivision of current mankind without any time depth, from a purely classificatory viewpoint. Several objects are put in front of us, and we are asked to reduce their multiplicity into a lesser number of categories. Why are we asked to do so? First because, if successful, it will provide us with an efficient means of a quicker and easier memorization of the attributes of the individual objects. Instead of having to memorize their characteristics object by object, our mind has only to apprehend the general qualities of each class, and within the latter framework the peculiarities of each object. Classification is a natural tendency of the mind, a highly satisfying procedure because it saves much time and pain. Another reason is that it makes generalization possible. If we reduced objects numbered one to 100 into ten classes labelled a to j, themselves grouped in three superclasses A, B, and C, we could speak of superclass B or class d in terms of what is common to all objects in these groups.

Classification by itself does not produce any new knowledge concerning individual things: it is only a mental operation performed on existing knowledge. If the things are not such as to allow their grouping into classes, the failure to classify them may be felt as frustrating, but it does not imply any loss of knowledge. For some things are not necessarily of a nature to permit classification.

Suppose we consider things by their qualitative aspects alone. For example, they are white or red, square or round, metal or wood. A classification based on the three properties will be useful only if there are several things in at least one of the eight possible classes. If they only differ quantitatively in a continuous scale, the problem is more complex. If we consider just one quantitative property, classification is possible only if the things cluster into several groups located at different heights along the scale. In order to be useful, one more condition must be satisfied: the range occupied by a cluster on the scale may not exceed the length of the empty spaces between it and adjacent clusters. Suppose, for example, we are trying to classify things by their linear size, and that the total range runs from 10 to 70 cm, with an empty space on the scale from 40 to 45 cm. Two clusters appear, but two objects belonging to different clusters (of 39 and 50 cm for example) may be much more alike than they are to many members of their own cluster. If size is considered a criterion of affinity, what is the validity of generalizing about short and long things?

Cluster analyis still applies to the case of more than one quantitative variable under consideration, but the eventual correlations between them have to be taken into account. For two variables, a graphical representation is still possible; a representation in space can be built for three variables; for a higher number of properties we can no more visualize the situation but we can make use, if a number of assumptions are satisfied, of efficient statistics, like the generalized distance (D^2) of Mahalanobis which still permits cluster analysis. Again a classification is serviceable only if clusters do appear, and if inter-cluster distances are higher than intra-cluster ones.

Turning now to our problem, human taxonomy, what are the things we wish to classify? Human populations, if we accept the proposed definition of race. They are themselves an assemblage of individuals. For no attribute can they be studied qualitatively: owing to human polymorphism, mankind cannot be subdivided in one group with zero per cent and one group with 100 per cent frequencies for any one character. The properties used for a classification will therefore be expressed as frequencies or means. Cluster analysis will be the basic taxonomic procedure.

How many characters shall we use for building a classification? If we use very few characters, human variability is such that markedly different classifications may emerge from different sets of characters. A sufficient number of characters must be considered in order to make it improbable that including an additional one would alter the picture; this can be tested with currently known characters and with new ones when discovered.

All characters are not equally efficient for taxonomic purposes. Their efficiency depends in particular on their world range of variation. The wider their interpopulational variability, the lower will be the number required for a consistent classification. As said before, gene pools are what we really want to classify. Gene frequencies are consequently the ideal materials. Characters for which gene frequencies have been computed on a large scale do not unfortunately constitute that array of highly variable features concerning the most variable aspects of man needed for the attempt to achieve a satisfactory classification: Those traits or characters were imposed on us by the accidents of their discovery. Many important aspects of human variation can be studied today only through metric variables that cannot be translated into gene frequencies. Furthermore, the environment intervenes in influencing the expression of most of them, and even if the environmental factor could be removed or controlled, identical effects could result from different gene pools. On the other hand, a set of metric variables can be chosen in order to represent the main variable traits of human morphology (for example from the results of a factor analysis) which are relatively not very sensitive to environment. If the clusters eventually observed from such a set and from a set of currently computable gene frequencies clearly differ, there is a strong suspicion that one or both of them are inadequate for a comprehensive analysis of overall distances.

The ideal technique of the classifier described in this way, the main question may now be asked: Are human populations such that they form clusters within which the distances are less than the inter-cluster distances? Only regional cluster analysis of human populations has been published so far. I am responsible for one of them (Hiernaux 1956), made on fifteen populations which fill a circumscribed area in central Africa. Mean interpopulational variability in this area is especially high, a fact that increases the chances of successful classification. In fact, one cluster of two closely related populations (the Tutsi of Rwanda and those of Burundi) is clearly apart, but the remaining thirteen populations allow no further clustering, despite their considerable variability. Represented on a two-dimensional plane, their position would clump without any clear internal cleavage, however great the distance between some of the plotted populations (in terms of classical anthropology, the group includes populations so different as to call the one "Hamiticized Bantu" and the other "Pygmoid"). I am now trying to extend the analysis to all Africa south of the Sahara. Only a crude kind of statistics can be applied owing to the nature of most published data. Only very preliminary statements are permissible at the present stage of development. It can, however, be said that an uncleavable clump, showing jagged edges, is the general picture, with maybe a few isolated clusters (the Bushmen, for example). I doubt that any useful classification will emerge beyond the separation of the eventual few clusters.

Such a situation is surely not peculiar to Africa. The total variability of European populations is less. A superficial examination of published data on Asian anthropology does not give the impression that many isolated clusters would emerge. Clustering would undoubtedly be favored in America by the vastly different origins of its current inhabitants, but the races so defined on a continental basis would lose much of their originality when introduced into the world picture.

Following the above procedure would there emerge something resembling the classical subdivision of mankind into three main groups: Whites, Blacks, and Yellows (or whatever more sophisticated terms are used)? I doubt it. We know of so many populations that do not fit into the picture! Adding more "oids" to this three-fold primary subdivision would not improve it. The subdivision into nine geographic races (i.e. "the taxonomic unit immediately below the species") proposed by Garn (1961) is no more satisfactory: it only shifts the problems to a lower level. Just as Indians could not be classed with the Black or White races of the ternary system, numerous populations are unclassifiable in a nine-fold subdivision because they are peripheral to several geographical races. It seems highly probable to me that the more races we create the more unclassifiable populations there would be at fewer and fewer levels of differences, until we should reach a state of subdivision close to an enumeration of all existing populations, i.e., the units to be classified.

Though not based on a systematic testing, my impression is thus that an attempt at a classification of contemporary mankind along the lines here indicated would yield very poor results: an uncleavable mass of populations, however large the constellation they form, and a few isolated clusters, which alone could be called races. This impression was gained from considering monofactorial characters as well as multifactorial ones. Unclassifiability seems to me inherent in the modalities of human variability. What can be built from a detailed knowledge of human variability is a diagnostic key. There are no two identical gene pools nor two phenotypically identical populations. By a system of successive dichotomies any population could be identified, as could also any human being since the probability of finding two identical individuals is exceedingly low (the exception of monozygotic twins is only an apparent one, since genetically they constitute but one individual). But a diagnostic key and an efficient classification are two different devices, though constructed from similar materials.

Many race classifications used to-day did not result from a cluster analysis, but reflect an attempt to extract from the anthropological data the peculiarities common to most populations of vast geographical areas. This is, for example, the case of the classification into thirteen races falling into seven main groups proposed by Boyd (1963), in which the races are defined by characteristic ranges of gene frequencies. Such a splitting of mankind essentially belongs to a diagnostic key. Its equation to a genuine classification is not clear. The conditions necessary for a valid classification will be examined later.

Probably many will find the requirement of a maximal intra-cluster distance lower than the minimal inter-cluster one too exacting. But again what is the usefulness of a classification of races A and B if we know that some populations of race A are nearer to some of race B than to some of their own race?

Though seemingly extreme, the position here expressed concerning the intrinsic resistance of contemporary mankind to any coherent taxonomic subdivision might be partly shared by many who use racial terminology. Dobzhansky (1962), commenting on Livingstone's (1962) paper on the nonexistence of human races (in which arguments similar to mine are set forth), agrees that "if races have to be discrete units, then there are no races," but is satisfied by races as a category of biological classification so vague that ". . . how many [races] should be recognized is a matter of convenience and hence of judgement." Boyd (1950) states: "Whatever races we choose to distinguish will be almost entirely arbitrary, and their distribution will depend on the particular characteristic on which we choose to base them." Washburn (1963) expresses the opinion that "since races are open systems which are intergrading, the number of races will depend on the purpose of the classification." Though defining a local race as a breeding population, Garn (1961) does not apply this concept when listing local races. For example, he considers the Bantu as a local race, while Bantu breeding populations number more than one hundred. In fact, he applies his former concept of a local race (Garn and Coon 1955): "our enumeration [of local races] depends on the minimum size of the population units we wish to consider," thus introducing a highly arbitrary element into his system. There seems to be no basic theoretical disagreement between these authors' views and those exposed here. The difference lies in the fact that they consider it useful to separate into discrete units, in a somewhat arbitrary manner, the open intergrading systems that they record (there is no escaping it: if you put a label, be it a name, a letter or a number, on something, you make it discrete). What I question is this: If any racial classification is arbitrary, for what purpose can it be of any use? Why spend so much time and effort building a classification, knowing that many others, not any worse, could be opposed to it, and that it runs the risk not only of being useless but also harmful by conveying the erroneous impression that it makes generalization possible?

Washburn's (1963) answer is: "Race is a useful concept only if one is concerned with the kind of anatomical, genetic, and structural differences which were in time past important in the origin of races. . . . If classification is to have a purpose, we may look backward to the explanation of the differences between people structural, anatomical, physiological differences—and then the concept of race is useful, but it is useful under no other circumstances, as far as I can see." A similar answer is given by Newman (1963): "If indeed the population is the proper unit for biological study—and we have been told this many times in the past 15 years—much of the older racial work that was not so oriented needs to be rescrutinized, screened, and then appraised against the yardstick of modern populational studies. This is laborious work and would be worth it only for the understanding of phylogeny and race process that come from building a taxonomy from the bottom upward."

Human Taxonomy and Phylogeny

These statements lead us to question the possibility and usefulness of human taxonomy in the light of a criterion not yet referred to here: Racial classification is useful if it reflects phylogeny.

Let us first examine the conditions required for making a

phylogenetic classification of populations possible. The basic one is this: Evolution must have taken the form of a growing tree. The current populations represent the terminal twigs; the bough common to several twigs may be called a race, the larger limb common to several boughs corresponds to a higher taxonomic unit, and so on until we reach the trunk which represents the human species. Infraspecific evolution takes this form only when the species splits into several groups which are exposed to different evolutionary forces and events under complete or effective genetic isolation, with eventual further splitting under similar conditions of differentiation in isolation. The process of raciation in this mode of evolution is the same as that of speciation, but represents only its initial stage; speciation is attained when and if the accumulated differences have reached the level at which fertile cross-matings no longer occur even when the subgroups come together again. Under such conditions, if we could follow each population back into the past, it would be possible to build an impregnable phylogenetic classification, which would reflect the dynamics of race formation. Would it be possible to derive a phylogenetic tree from data on contemporary populations? Only if great care is taken in the dynamic explanation of differences. The overall distances used for a horizontal classification may be misleading, especially if few characters are considered: each adaptative feature responds to its own specific environmental stimuli, convergence may occur, and the accident of random drift may, in one generation, strongly differentiate two newly separated populations. The difficulty cannot be bypassed by trying to use nonadaptive characters only: even if they could be identified with certainty, the fact remains that their frequencies are especially sensitive to the long-lasting effects of drift, and we should thus reduce the possibilities of classification, since adaptation is an important process of differentiation. By and large however, if human evolution had been of the type described, a taxonomy built from the current characteristics of human populations would be of great help in the understanding of their phylogeny. Moreover, under such conditions, the chances are large that clear-cut clustering would correspond to characteristic constellations of gene frequencies. The limiting conditions to such a general correspondence between ultimate clusters and characteristic constellations seem to be felt by Boyd (1963) who, while defining races by characteristic constellations, writes: "Racial differentiation is the end result of the action of natural selection on the raw material provided by random mutations in a population sufficiently isolated genetically." But the fact is that no nonarbitrary general classification of mankind is available, and what we know of the migratory habits of man, and of the extent to which population mixture took place, altogether explains why no systematic subdivision of races is possible, and eliminates the hope that a general phylogeny-reflecting classification could be constructed. Human evolution did not take the form of a growing tree, at least, not in recent times. The general picture is not one of isolated groups differentiating in circumscribed areas. Mixture occurred many times in many places between the most various populations brought into contact by human mobility. The tendency toward high adaptive specialization was balanced again and again by migration, and by man's power to transform his environment. Even if we could reconstruct the intricate succession of mixtures that contributed to each living population, the final picture would look like a reticulum more than a tree, and a reticulum defies dichotomizing subdivision.

There have always been forces acting toward raciation, but they conduced to genuine races (in the sense of well-individualized clusters of populations) only here and there. I have already cited the Bushmen as a possible race that could emerge from an analysis of African variability; if this is confirmed, it would mean that this group experienced a differentiating evolution combined with a high degree of isolation. The Bushmen are in the long run facing either extinction or disappearance as a race through mixture, while maybe another race is in process of individualization somewhere else in the world. The few genuine races that could emerge from a cluster analysis of living mankind might not be those of tomorrow, nor those of yesterday.

If the preceding views are correct, the recent biological history of mankind can be visualized as an immense irregular reticulum growing upward; here and there at different time levels a stem grows away from the mass but is later embodied by it. Human populations are such that they defy general classification because of their phylogenetic history. To force them to fit into a classificatory scheme by overlooking a large part of the data can only lead to a grossly distorted idea of their phylogeny.

Conclusion

From whatever viewpoint one approaches the question of the applicability of the concept of race to mankind, the modalities of human variability appear so far from those required for a coherent classification that the concept must be considered as of very limited use. In my opinon, to dismember mankind into races as a convenient approximation requires such a distortion of the facts that any usefulness disappears: on the contrary, only the harm done by such practices remains. They tend to force our minds into erroneous channels of thinking, or, if we manage to retain any lucidity, to enter a maze of distinctions and restrictions.

To give up all general racial classifications would mean for anthropology freeing itself from blinkers it has too long worn, and focusing all its energy on its actual goal: the understanding of human variability, as it really is.

References

Boyd, W. C. 1950. *Genetics and the Races of Man*. Boston, D. C. Heath & Co.

Boyd, W. C. 1963. Genetics and the human race. *Science* 140:1057–1064.

Coon, C. S., S. M. Garn and J. B. Birdsell. 1950. *Races*. Springfield, Thomas.

Czekanowski, J. 1962. The theoretical assumptions of Polish anthropology and the morphological facts. *Current Anthropology* 3:481–494.

Dobzhansky, Th. 1962. Comment on "The Non-existence of human races" by F. B. Livingstone. *Current Anthropology* 3:279–280.

Dunn, L. C. and Th. Dobzhansky. 1952. *Heredity, Race and Society*. Rev. ed. New York, New American Library.

Frankenberg, G. von. 1956. *Menschenrassen und Menschentum*. Berlin, Safari-Verlag.

Garn, S. M. and C. S. Coon. 1955. On the number of races of mankind. *American Anthropologist* 57:996–1001.

Garn, S. M. 1961. *Human Races*. Springfield, Thomas.

Gloor, P. A. 1961–62. Premiers résultats d'une enquête sur la structure raciale régionale en Suisse. *Bull, suisse Anthrop. et Ethnol.* 38, pp. 5 et 6.

Hiernaux, J. 1956. *Analyse de la variation des caractères physiques humains en une région de l'Afrique centrale: Ruanda-Urundi et Kivu*. Ann. Mus. roy. Congo belge, Sci. de l'Homme, Anthrop., 3.

———. 1962. Le concept de race en anthropologie physique. *Actes VIe Congr. int. Sci. anthrop. et ethnol.* (Paris 1960) 1:471–477.

Howells, W. 1959. *Mankind in the Making*. New York, Doubleday.

Livingstone, F. B. 1962. On the non-existence of human races. *Current Anthropology* 3:279–281.

Marquer, P. 1963. Contribution à l'étude anthropologique du peuple basque et up problème de ses origines raciales. *Bull. Soc. Anthrop. Paris* 4, XI: 1–240.

Newman, M. T. 1963. Geographic and micrographic races. *Current Anthropology* 5: 189–207.

Vallois, H. V. 1953. "Race" in *Anthropology Today* (edited by Koeber), 145–162. Chicago, University of Chicago Press.

Washburn, S. L. 1963. The study of race. *American Anthropologist* 65, 521–531.

Wierciński, A. 1962. The racial analysis of human populations in relation to their ethnogenesis. *Current Anthropology* 3: 2 and 9–20.

IV On the Nonexistence
of Human Races

FRANK B. LIVINGSTONE

In the last decade there has been a remarkable increase in our knowledge of the complexities of human genetic variability. To an increasing number of anthropologists the concept of race seems to be losing its usefulness in describing this variability. In fact, for the human populations among which some of us have worked, it seems impossible even to divide these populations into races. At the same time a growing minority of biologists in general are advocating a similar position with regard to the usefulness of the concept of subspecies for classifying such diverse organisms as grackles, martens, and butterflies (Brown, 1957; Hagmeier, 1958; Gillham, 1956). Although there appears to have been a minimum of communication between anthropologists and biologists on this common problem, many of the arguments of the two groups are quite similar. It should be pointed out that the two similar positions on subspecific variation do not imply that there is no biological or genetic variability among the populations of organisms which comprise a species, but simply that this variability does not conform to the discrete packages

Reprinted with revisions from *Current Anthropology*, Vol. 3, pp. 279-281, 1962.

labelled races or subspecies. For man the position can be stated in other words: There are no races, there are only clines.

The term, race, has had a long history of anthropological usage and it can be generally defined as referring to a group of local or breeding populations within a species. Thus, it is a taxonomic term for subspecific groupings greater than the local population. Most anthropologists today use a genetic definition of races as populations which differ in the frequency of some genes.

The term, race, or its newer synonym, geographical race, is used in a similar way with reference to biological species other than man. Where the term is used, it can be considered as approximately synonymous with the term, subspecies. In 1953 Wilson and Brown first suggested discarding the concept of subspecies since it did not accord with the facts. Their main argument was that the genetic variation among the local populations of a species was discordant.

Variation is concordant if the geographic variation of the genetic characters is correlated, so that a classification based on one character would reflect the variability in any other. Such a pattern of variation is almost never found among the local populations of a wide-ranging species, although it is usually found among related relatively allopatric species. ?

Thus, although it is possible to divide a group of related species into discrete units, namely the species, it is impossible to divide a single species into groups larger than the panmictic population. The causes of intraspecific biological variation are different from those of interspecific variation and to apply the term subspecies to any part of such variation is not only arbitrary or impossible but tends to obscure the explanation of this variation. If one genetic character is used, it is possible to divide a species into subspecies according to the variation in this character. If two characters are used, it may still be possible, but there will be some "problem populations," which, if you are an anthropologist, will be labelled composite or mixed. As the number of characters increases it becomes more nearly impossible to determine what the "actual races really are."

In addition to being a concept used to classify human variability, race has also been overworked as an explanation of this variability. When a particular blood group gene or hair form is found to be characteristic of the populations of a particular region, it is frequently "explained" as being a "racial" character. This type of explanation means, in other words, that this particular set of human populations possess this character, while it is absent in the rest of humanity, because of the close common ancestry of the former. At times many characteristics which were thought to be racial have been found in many widely separated populations, so that the explanation in terms of race required the assumption of lengthy migrations. In this way race or common ancestry and migration have been used to explain much of the genetic variability among human populations. Unfortunately such explanations neither accord with our knowledge of the population structure and movements of hunters and gatherers, nor take into consideration the basic cause of biological variation, natural selection.

The incompatibility between race and natural selection has been recognized for a long time; so that if one's major aim were to discover the races of man, one has to disregard natural selection. Thus, nonadaptive characters were sought and, in some instances, considered found. But the recognition of the role of natural selection has in the past ten years changed the course of research into human variability; or at least it has changed the thinking of the "aracial ultrapolymorphists."

Recently there have been two somewhat different attempts to resolve the dilemmas created by our new knowledge and outlook and still retain the term, race. On the one hand, Dobzhansky (1962) appears to want to apply the term, racial variability, to any differences in gene frequencies among human populations, a usage which accords with the genetic definition of race as stated above. Since all human populations most likely differ in the frequency of some gene, this position implies that each population would be a separate race; but to Dobzhansky it is a matter of convenience as to how many we call races. Such a usage also implies that any number of racial classifications of the same populations but based on different gene frequencies are "equally valid" or useful. It should be noted that this is a quite different concept of race than previous usage and seems as unfortunate to Hiernaux (1963 and the present volume pp. 30–45) as it does to me. But if applied rigorously to the human populations of the world it would result in much the same description of human genetic variability as the clinal analysis advocated in this paper but with the description in words and not in numbers as a clinal analysis would be.

On the other hand, Garn (1961), although paying homage to the genetic definition of race, has attempted to demonstrate the existence of nine specific geographical races, but the question of whether there are nine or nineteen such races is not arbitrary or up to the classifier or dependent on the genetic character used in the classification. These are taxonomic races, but "taxonomic races must bear correspondence to natural races, mirroring nature rather than lecturing her" (Garn, 1963, p. 197), which I think it is fair to say, Garn thinks his geographical races do. Also some of these geographical races "approach true subspecies" (p. 198), and these races, and not others, exist because "the first and foremost fact governing the existence of a geographical race is that it has distinct geographical limits coinciding with major reproductive barriers" (p. 198), which Garn's races presumably do. Thus, according to Garn, there are natural races to which our taxonomic races should correspond, and although the number of races may vary through time, it is still fixed at any one time. Since the

existence, validity, or utility of this racial classification is
almost entirely dependent on the existence of these major
reproductive barriers to gene flow, it seems to me that Garn
should present a careful, detailed analysis of these barriers to
demonstrate the existence of his geographical races. Aside
from a few vague references to the "scarcely inhabited up-
lands" (Garn, 1961, p. 15), in Western Asia or the deserts of
Africa, however, such a demonstration is not forthcoming.
Thus, it is rather difficult to contest the existence of the nine
geographical races, but I think it can be argued that at present
these "major reproductive barriers" do not exist and most
likely have existed even less in the past. For example, an analysis of the populations and/or genes in the Sahara Desert certainly indicates that the desert is not a major reproductive
barrier, although there may be fewer people or populations
inhabiting it. In addition, the utter wasteland which characterizes most parts of the Sahara today is a rather recent phenomenon and due in large part to human occupation. A short
5000 years ago pastoralists occupied much of the Sahara, and
it was perhaps one of the most populated parts of Africa.
Prior to these pastoralists, the rich African fauna inhabited
most of the Sahara and North Africa and provided probably
the best hunting in the whole continent, as the great numbers
of archeological finds attest (Mauny, 1955; Forde-Johnston,
1959). The concept of race seems to me to be of no use in
describing or explaining human genetic variability in this
region today. The retention of this obsolete concept has
caused a recent analysis of the genetic variability among
Saharan populations to label the Teda as having "Berber blood
in Negro bodies" and the Moors as having "negroid blood in
morphologically Berber bodies" (Briggs, 1957, pp. 20–21).
Such a description only confuses the issue and hence is worse
than useless.

Such a description of the bodies and blood of a human

population also implies an explanation of their particular characteristics, which is based on common ancestry and/or mixture with the race involved. The advocates of the validity of the concept of race recognize the great genetic variability which occurs among the populations of the Sahara, Sudan, and Ethiopia, and even refer to these areas as a "clinal zone." The usual explanation of these clines in terms of race and mixture is so widely accepted—even among cultural anthropologists and the general public—that Murdock (1959, p. 9) can state baldly with respect to Ethiopians, "The Cushites have long since incorporated a not insubstantial infusion of Negroid blood. This reveals itself in different ways in different tribes. Thus the lowland Somali are much darker than the peoples of Highland Ethiopia but have hair that is wavy or occasionally straight and only rarely kinky, whereas this typically Negroid form prevails in sixty to seventy percent of the plateau population." This statement clearly indicates that the clines in these characters are discordant. For this reason it is impossible to explain these clines or this genetic variability solely in terms of race and mixture. If a population is X per cent Negro in one characteristic it must be X per cent in all characters for this to be an adequate explanation. If it is not, other factors of evolutionary change must be involved. One could invoke random genetic drift but the more likely explanation is natural selection. I think this analysis of human genetic variation in racial terms aptly illustrates the inadequacy of this kind of analysis. As an illustration of how our increasing knowledge of biochemical genetics increases this inadequacy, I refer the reader to a recent series of papers on Ethiopian populations (*American Journal of Physical Anthropology*, 1962, pp. 168–208B). Furthermore, this increase in knowledge clearly contradicts Coon's statement that "To me, at least, it is encouraging to know that biochemistry divides us into the same subspecies that we recognize on the basis of other criteria" (Coon, 1962, p. 663). It is discouraging, to me at least, that anyone would make such a statement.

Garn (1961) also seems to regard some biological characteristics as having a similar racial explanation. Garn (1961, p. 16) states that while "Certain human differences transcend geographical race, and are more meaningfully distributed with respect to climate or disease. . . . A geographical race is a collection of populations whose similarities are due to long-continued confinement within set geographical limits." Although these similarities are not outlined in detail, Garn does imply that some biological characteristics are due to natural selection through climate and disease, while others—the racial traits— are not. Natural races thus only reflect variability in certain traits, and any racial classification can only describe a part of human genetic variability and seemingly explain it.

For animal populations other than man, Mayr (1963) has also considered the problems associated with the concept of subspecies, although Mayr feels that "These questions are of little evolutionary interest" (p. 350). He gives a definition of subspecies as "an aggregate of local populations of a species, inhabiting a geographic subdivision of the range of the species, and differing taxonomically from other populations of the species" (p. 348). Mayr thinks that the subspecies category is such a convenient taxonomic device, this accounts for the great reluctance to abandon it. Although it is still convenient, Mayr (1963, p. 349) warns "It must be realized at all times, however, that in many cases the subspecies is an artifact and that it is not a 'unit of evolution.' Nor should the subspecies be confused with phenomena of a very different nature, such as character gradients (clines)." I think it is fair to say that both Garn (1961) and Coon (1962) conceive of human races as "units of evolution," in fact the major units of human evolution, which is the major source of confusion as Mayr says.

Mayr continues his discussion of genetic variation within a species by separating this variation into three categories: 1) clinal variation, 2) geographic isolates, 3) hybrid belts or zones of intergradation, which he further divides into primary and secondary zones of intergradation (p. 360). According to Mayr, "Whether a subspecies is part of a cline or is isolated completely by geographic barriers is, however, of decisive influence on its evolutionary potential" (p. 366). Thus, some genetic variation within species is subspecific, some clinal, and some associated with primary or secondary zones of intergradation, which, however, might exist between subspecies.

In addition to being a method of describing genetic variability among the populations of a species, each of Mayr's concepts implies an explanation of the variability which it labels. This seems to be particularly so when such variability is said to be associated with primary or secondary zones of intergradation (Mayr, 1963, p. 369). Mayr's different concepts of the way in which to explain genetic variability among the populations of a species accord with the mathematical theory of population genetics, which is advocated here, but again, like Dobzhansky, Mayr's analysis attempts to apply words or labels to different kinds of variability or "phenomena." However, the major argument of this paper is that at present we can be much more precise and, further, that these obsolete labels are inhibiting scientific advances in this field.

I do not think these arguments or the problems they face are of "little evolutionary significance" but quite the opposite. The explanation of the genetic variability among human populations is a central problem of physical anthropology, and there are other methods of describing and explaining this variability which do not utilize the concept of race or which simply attempt to label different kinds of genetic variability. Human genetic variability can be described in terms of the concepts of cline and morphism (Huxley, 1955) or poly-

morphism which is becoming more widely used to denote the
same thing. The variability in the frequency of any gene can
be plotted in the same way that temperature is plotted on a
weather map, and this description of genetic variability can
describe all of it and implies no explanation whatsoever. Then
one can attempt to explain this variability by the mathematical
theory of population genetics. This is a very general theory
and is capable of explaining all racial or gene frequency differences, although of course for any particular gene the exact
magnitudes of factors, mutation, natural selection, gene drift,
and gene flow, which control gene frequency differences are
not known. All genes mutate, drift, flow, and for a given
environment have fitnesses associated with their various genotypes. Hence differences in the frequency of any gene among
a series of populations can be explained by these general factors which control gene frequency change. Gene frequency
clines can result from many different types of interaction
between the general factors which control gene frequencies.
For example, a cline may be due to: 1) the recent advance of
an advantageous gene; 2) gene flow between populations
which inhabit environments with different equilibrium frequencies for the gene; or 3) a gradual change in the equilibrium value of the gene along the cline. The theoretical analysis
of clines has barely begun but there seems to be no need for
the concept of race in this analysis.

I want to emphasize that in contrast to racial analysis,
clinal analysis is a method which can describe all gene frequency differences. Even if one or several genes are completely absent in one population and 100 per cent in the next
adjacent population, these differences can still be described
as clines albeit very steep ones. But if the variability of a particular gene is continuous from Cairo to Capetown, its variability cannot be described in terms of race, or if two genes
vary discordantly, the races set up on the basis of one do not

describe the variability in the other. Just as Galileo's measurements and experiments paved the way for Newton's laws of motion, which totally replaced the Aristotelian laws of motion concerned as they were with describing the nature of bodies and their "essences," our newer genetic knowledge and the measurement of gene frequencies will replace the studies on the nature or essence of race and the mathematical theory of population genetics will replace the Linnaean system of nomenclature. Newton's laws can describe and explain all motion, just as clines can describe all genetic variability and coupled with the modern theory of evolution explain it. Linnaeus was given a medal 200 years ago for "discovering the essence of genera" which I think is an apt expression of the Aristotelian mode of thought and concept of the universe. In 1963 Newman and Dobzhansky are still attempting to discover the nature of race or as Dobzhansky says (1950, p. 101) "defining the essence of race. . . ." Dobzhansky (1963) has characterized my position as having "discovered that races of man do not exist," but I have never "discovered" anything. The concepts of a culture are primarily a function of the level of measurement and observation within the culture. "Races" of man unfortunately exist in the United States, and race as a concept of Western Civilization exists just as much as God or the $\sqrt{-1}$. Much of the discussion on the existence of race reminds me of the obituary in *Time* Magazine (January 11, 1963) of Arthur O. Lovejoy. When the late Professor Lovejoy was asked at a government investigation if he believed in God, he promptly rattled off thirty-three definitions of God and asked the questioner which one he had in mind. But of course it really didn't matter to the questioner. To avow a belief in the existence of God simply assured one's participation in the socio-cultural system, in which everyone knows that God exists out there but we humans are just too ignorant to perceive or define Him accurately. It is likewise with races; they exist but we haven't discovered or defined them yet.

Just as races do not exist but are only part of a general theory concocted by human beings to explain or render intelligible their observations, so the concepts and theorems of the mathematical theory of population genetics do not exist in the same sense. Any scientific theory can be considered as a mathematical or logical system with no reference to reality. It consists of certain basic or primitive terms and axioms from which are derived the major statements or content of the theory, the theorems. Such a theory is fitted to reality by operational definitions of the basic terms so that there are rules to measure random mating or the mutation rate just as there are rules to measure mass or acceleration (see R. L. Wilder, 1952, for an exposition of the nature of scientific theories). In this way the application of any scientific theory is a function of the measuring instruments and experiments of the culture at that time. According to this particular view, I don't think it is legitimate to say that anthropologists and geneticists have "discovered" breeding populations in the last twenty years.

The concept of breeding population when considered as part of the mathematical theory of population genetics pertains to nothing in reality. But when combined with the concepts of gene frequency, random mating, etc., further concepts such as the Hardy-Weinberg Law or the principle of random gene drift can be logically derived. The latter are more or less the theorems of population genetics and are the logical outcomes of the more basic concepts or axioms. The science of population genetics then attempts to apply this theory to bodies of data and to attempt to determine which group of individuals in a particular area fits most closely the concept of breeding population, but the function of this concept of the theory is not to divide up or label reality, but to explain it. Of course, the concepts of the mathematical theory of population genetics have been developed from the data and findings of a particular sphere of reality and are approximations to these data. But they can also be considered solely as logical concepts and studied as a formal system with no reference to this reality. As Medawar (1960) has remarked, this theory has great generality in biology and in that science occupies a position analogous to Newton's Laws in physical science. An infinite population randomly mating without selection, mutation, or gene flow is analogous to Newton's body moving without friction at a constant velocity.

In applying the theory of population genetics to humanity, the species is divided into breeding populations although for any area or group of people this concept may be difficult to apply. It is likely that each breeding population will prove to be genetically unique, so that all will be racially distinct in Dobzhansky's terms. But this is not the general use of the concept of race in biology, and the concept has not in the past been associated with this theory of human diversity. Race has instead been considered as a concept of the Linnaean system of classification within which it is applied to groups of populations within a species. To apply a concept of the Linnaean system to a group of populations implies something about the evolutionary history of these populations, and it also implies that these populations are similar in whatever characters were used to classify them together because of close common ancestry.

For years such racial traits were considered to be relatively nonadaptive and were the property of the physical anthropologists, while at the same time the geneticists were concerned with characters which were due to the presence of a single gene and which were for the most part deleterious. Much of the early work in human genetics was done on such characters as achondroplasia, albinism, alcaptonuria, and brachydactyly. Most of these deleterious genes occur in low frequencies in most populations and their explanation seems to be a balance of mutation to them and selection against them. These were considered "bad" genes but once in a great while a "good" gene would appear and completely replace its allele. Although the sickle cell gene has changed the outlook of geneticists, the idea that there are different kinds of inherited traits which require different explanations persists today. Coon (1962) has even introduced a new division into racial and evolutionary characters. But to use an overworked cliché, a gene is a gene is a gene, and all genes are subject to the factors outlined previously which control gene frequencies. Hence the mathematical theory of population genetics applies to all genes, racial, deleterious, evolutionary, etc.

But science progresses. Just as the theory of population genetics is gaining acceptance, the pace of biological research is such that our measuring instruments are beginning to reach beyond the concepts. Newton's Laws when first accepted were considered to be "truth" or "facts," but when the measuring instruments began to get above and below their sphere of application, Einstein's equations replaced them. Similarly the mathematical theory of population genetics evolved around and was based on the concept of a gene as a bead on a chromosomal string. It was the unit which mutated, recombined, and functioned—at first to produce one enzyme but now one polypeptide chain. And it was a satisfactory unit for the experimental genetics of the day which consisted of animal breeding and observation of hereditary characters. But now as these discrete units have become a rather continuous strand of DNA, the question can be asked, do these units with the aforementioned properties exist? Obviously not (Benzer, 1962), and it has been suggested that we discuss mutons, recons, and cistrons in place of genes. It would appear that any unit above the individual base pair is arbitrary. Hence the mathematical theory of population genetics is almost obsolete before it begins to be accepted. But to me this is only one vivid example of the maxim that "Yesterday's science is today's common sense and tomorrow's nonsense." For the concept of race and the intraspecific application of the Linnaean system of classification, tomorrow is here.

References

American Journal of Physical Anthropology, 1962, A survey of some genetical characteristics in Ethiopian tribes, 20:168–208B.

Benzer, S. 1962. The fine structure of the gene. *Scientific American* 206:70–84.

Briggs, L. C. 1957. A review of the physical anthropology of the Sahara and its prehistoric implications. *Man* 57:20–23.

Brown, W. L. Jr. 1957. Centrifugal speciation. *Quarterly Review of Biology* 32:247–277.

Coon, C. S. 1962. *The Origin of Races.* New York, Knopf.

Dobzhansky, T. 1950. The genetic nature of differences among men in S. Persons, editor, *Evolutionary Thought in America.* New Haven, Yale 86–155.

——. 1962. Comment on Livingstone. *Current Anthropology* 3:279–280.

——. 1963. Comment on Newman. *Current Anthropology* 4:197–198.

Forde-Johnston. 1959. *Neolithic Cultures of North Africa.* Liverpool, Liverpool University Press.

Garn, S. M. 1961. *Human Races.* Springfield, Thomas.

——. 1963. Comment on Newman. *Current Anthropology* 4:197–198.

Gillham, N. W. 1956. Geographic variation and the subspecies concept in butterflies. *Systematic Zoology* 5:110–120.

Hagmeier, E. M. 1958. The inapplicability of the subspecies concept in the North American Marten. *Systematic Zoology* 7:1–7.

Hiernaux, J. 1963. Comment on Newman. *Current Anthropology* 4:198–199.

Huxley, J. S. 1955. Morphism and evolution. *Heredity* 9:1–52.

Mauny, R. 1957. Repartition de la grande "faune ethiopienne" du Nord-Ouest Africain du Paleolithique a nos jours. Proceedings of the 3rd Pan African Congress of Prehistory, 1955, 102–105.

Mayr, E. 1963. *Animal Species and their Evolution.* Cambridge, Harvard.

Medawar, P. B. 1960. *The Future of Man.* London, Methuen.

Murdock, G. P. 1959. *Africa.* New York, McGraw-Hill.

Newman, M. T. 1963. Geographic and microgeographic races. *Current Anthropology* 4:189–192.

Wilder, R. L. 1952. *Introduction to the Foundations of Mathematics.* New York, John Wiley.

Wilson, E. O. and Brown, W. L., Jr. 1953. The subspecies concept and its taxonomic application. *Systematic Zoology* 2:97–111.

V Lapp Racial Classifications as Scientific Myths*

ROBERT T. ANDERSON

Introduction[1]

Since Blumenbach first presented his five-fold classification of the varieties of man in 1781, scores of theorists have applied themselves to the problem of arranging human physical varieties into an orderly typology. Of the many classifications devised, all have found their nemesis in certain peoples who defy placement, such as the Polynesians, the Australians, the Veddas, the Pigmies, and the Lapps. These problem types have been dealt with in various ways. Kroeber, for example, followed the safe course of simply putting them into doubtful categories, and Hooton did not even mention the Lapps in *Up From the Ape* (1946). In general, however, racial theorists have faced up to the problem and have applied their metrical and logical methods to its solution. Because of

Reprinted from *Anthropological Papers of the University of Alaska,* Vol. 11. No. 1, December 1962.

1. I should like to express my appreciation to Professor T. D. McCown for earlier guidance in the physical anthropology of Lapland. Any shortcomings of the present paper, of course, are completely my own responsibility.

their amenability to speculation, and because so much attention has been paid to them, these racial types present interesting cases of the role of distortive subjectivity in the process of scientific inquiry. The following pages will be concerned with the Lapps as an illustrative example of persistent inaccuracies and misinterpretations that attained the level of scientific myths.

It is not the intent of this paper to present a comprehensive history of the racial classification of the Lapps, though the main trends of such a history will be evident. Recent genetic studies are completely beyond its scope. We have been content, rather, to show simply that non-objective factors have played their part, and that the part played has been disconcertingly large. To this end, attention focuses upon the history of the two most influential interpretations of Lapp race biology. The first one has now been abandoned. It held that the Lapps were relatives of the Finns and that both were originally Asiatics or Mongoloids. The second holds that the Lapps represent a remnant of an ur-race that was the ancestor of both modern Mongoloids and modern Caucasoids.

An Abandoned Interpretation

Writing in 1673, Johan Scheffer attributed the following characteristics to the Lapps: low stature, tawny (swarthy) complexion, extremely lean, thick heads and prominent foreheads, hollow and blare eyed, short, flat noses, wide mouths, flat faced, meagre cheeks, long chin, short, thin, straight, black hair, thin and short beard, very strong and active, stooped walk, superstitious, timerous and cowardly, and unfit for soldiery.

Concerning their racial status he wrote, "It is certain they don't deduce their Origine from the *Swedes,* there being no greater difference betwixt any thing on Earth . . ." (Scheffer, 1701, 37). He also noted that they differ as much from the Russians or Muscovites, and that the Norwegians have the same origin as the Swedes.

At that time there was a certain district in Finland called *Lappio* and therefore Wexovious concluded that the Lapps were descended from the Finns. "What Wexovious would infer here from the District called *Lappio,* as if the Laplanders had from thence got their Name, is a bare Surmise, founded upon very slender Reasons. . . . But what he says in general of their being descended from the *Finlanders,* is more than probable . . ." (Scheffer, 1701, 38). The reasons for maintaining that the Lapps are descended from the Finlanders are:

1. Both nations retain to this time the same name. *Sapme* or *Same* means Lapp in Lappish and *Suomi* means Finn in Finnish.
2. Both peoples have an ancient tradition that *Jumi* was the founder of their nations.
3. Their languages have a great affinity.
4. Their bodies and habits are also very much the same. Both have the same well set limbs, black hair, broad faces, stern countenances, laziness, superstitions, sorcery, temper, and clothes.
5. Such authorities as Conring and Wexovious confirm this relationship.

Since the ancient *Finlanders* came so near to the modern *Laplanders,* in every respect, they are questionless descended from the same stock. . . . What small difference there is observed betwixt them, must be ascribed to their different diet and climate (Scheffer, 1701, 41, 39).

Impressed with the effects of a harsh environment, Scheffer wrote, concerning *stature,*

Vostius alledges, as a reason for their lowness of stature, the violence of the cold, and that with a great deal of probability: For considering that the natural Heat is in a continual conflict with the violent cold, and is forced to exert all its activity to combat that enemy, and it is not sufficient to give due aid to the Excretion and Alimentation, which renders their bodies both lean and short: Tho' in my opinion, their food, which contains little fit for nourishment, may also contribute in a great measure to it ... (Scheffer, 1701, 24–5).

Concerning *skin color*,

What wonder is it, if those, who from their infancy are exposed to the smoak, should be of a tawny complexion? (Scheffer, 1701, 25).

Concerning their *posture*,

They seldom or never walk upright, but stoop continually, which is attributed to their sitting on the Ground in their low cottages (Scheffer, 1701, 27).

Concerning *faintheartedness*,

The reason that they are thus fainthearted is, that the excessive cold and miserable dyet renders their blood destitute of a sufficient quantity of spirits (Scheffer, 1701, 28).

Finally, Scheffer followed Conring in the opinion that the Laplanders, Finlanders, and Samoyeds are all of the same race and have "come out of *Asia* into the northern parts of Europe" (Scheffer, 1701, 38).

In the second edition of his famous dissertation, printed in 1781, J. F. Blumenbach presented for the first time his division of mankind into five varieties. Of these he wrote that the first variety is the largest and primeval one,

[it] embraces the whole of Europe, including the Lapps, whom I cannot in any way separate from the rest of the Europeans, when their appearance and their language bear such testimony to their Finnish origin ... (Blumenbach, 1865, 99).

In the third edition, however, printed in 1795, he had a different opinion. "The Caucasian variety includes the inhabitants of Europe—except the Lapps and the remaining descendants of the Finns (Blumenbach, 1865, 265). Furthermore, the Mongolian variety comprehends the Finnish populations of the cold part of Europe, including the Lapps (Blumenbach, 1865, 265–6).

The reason for this change is not mentioned. Scheffer is not cited and the theory is not espoused by any of the authors referred to. Probably he changed his mind as a result of reconsidering the data—possibly because he came into the possession of some additional skulls. In a publication of 1808 he noted the resemblances between Lapp and Mongolian crania. Concerning primary characters:

the skull large in proportion to the stature of the body; the form and appearance altogether such as prevail in the Mongolian Variety; the shape almost spherical or globose; the zygomatic bones extending outwards; the malar fossa, plane; the forehead broad; the chin rather prominent and acuminated (Prichard, 1841, Vol. III, 301).

Like Scheffer, Blumenbach was also impressed by the influence of environment.

We see nations which are reputed to be but colonies of one and the same stock have contracted in different climates different racial faces. Thus the Hungarians are considered to be the same primitive stock as the Lapps. The latter living in the furthest North have acquired the face so peculiar to the most northern nations; whereas the former living in the temperate zone, in the neighbourhood of Greece and Turkey, have gained a more elegant form of face (Blumenbach, 1865, 231).

Writing in 1822 Sir William Lawrence attributed certain characteristics to the Mongolian Variety, all but one of which were cranial. These were: forehead low and slanting; head square in form; lateral projection of malars; glabella and ossa nasi flat and small and on the same plane as the malar bones; scarcely any superciliary ridges; narrow nasal entrance; malar fossa forms but a slight excavation; alveolar edge of jaws obtusely arched in front; chin rather prominent; and short stature (Lawrence, 1822, 305).

Lawrence found that the characters of the Mongolian Variety "are strongly expressed in the skull of a Lapland female, and prove unequivocally that this race belongs to the Mongolian Variety" (Lawrence, 1822, 309). In another place he noted that the *"Caucasian Variety* includes all the ancient and modern Europeans, except the Laplanders and the rest of the Finnish race . . ." (Lawrence, 1822, 477). The latter statement contains the sole reference to the Finns, but it is sufficient to show that Lawrence was following earlier writers in his classification of the Finns, Lapps, and Mongols. Indeed, his debt to Blumenbach is not only expressed in his eloquent dedication, but his evaluation of the Lapp skull is footnoted to Blumenbach and his terminology—even his phraseology— attest the magnitude of this influence.

But, though he was prone to borrow, he was also capable of dissent. In discussing environmental causation he contended that neither climate nor the state of society can be given as affecting the "conformation and color of the body," since most modern European nations were barbarians until relatively recently, yet they have not changed physically (Lawrence, 1822, 453–5).

Instead, therefore, of accounting fore the dark colour, peculiar features, and stature of the Greenlander, Laplander, and Samoides, from their smoke, the dirt, their food, or the coldness of the climate, we . . . ascribe it to their descent from a race marked by the same characters as distinguish themselves. These tribes owe their origin to the Mongols: and retain in the north those marks of their descent found in the Chinese (Lawrence, 1822, 455).

This quotation not only illustrates his repudiation of environmentalism, but it also indicates contact with Scheffer, for his wording is obviously lifted largely from the English translation of *Lapponia*. Incidentally, it is curious to note that his description of the jaw as prominent is similar to observations on the Lapp jaw made by both Blumenbach and Scheffer, and contrasts with the modern observation that it is extremely shallow.

J. C. Prichard, in 1836, noted that "travelors have been struck by the different aspects of the Finns and the Lapps, and they have accounted for the phenomena in different ways. Some refuse to admit evidence of their consanguinity, though such evidence has been found sufficient to satisfy unprejudiced persons (Prichard, 1841, Vol. III, 297). In order to demonstrate this point he quoted at length from Scheffer and concluded in Scheffer's words: "their bodies and habits are very nearly the same . . ." (Prichard, 1841, Vol. III, 298).

But, though he clearly regards the Finns and the Lapps to be closely related, his view of their Mongoloid affinities is confused. For while he regards the Finns as having European features and complexion, many being handsome according to our ideas of beauty, he describes the Lapps as deviating from the usual characters of the European races and approximating to the Mongolian. Still, after quoting Blumenbach, he wrote, "that great physiologist was right in referring the Lapponic skull to the Mongolian type. We must admit that great diversity appears to have taken place in these two branches of one national stock" (Prichard, 1841, Vol. III, 308). It would appear, then, that he regards the Finns and the Lapps to have an Asiatic ancestry. He continues,

These observations and facts that tend to identify the Finns and the Lapps or to prove that they are originated from the same stock, are rendered the more interesting by the consideration that the physical diversity frequently, but not unusually, existing among them is very strongly marked" (Prichard, 1841, Vol. III, 300).

Furthermore, while admitting that the cause is difficult to discover, he feels that it is impossible to account for these diversities by reference to the hypothesis of intermixture with foreign nations. Neither can they be explained entirely as due to differences of climate or race (whatever he means by this!). He concludes,

It lies in the difference of external circumstances and agencies, which depends not on local but on moral conditions. The Finns are well fed and warmly clothed and sheltered from the inclemency of the winter cold, of which they further lessen the effect on their constitution by the frequent use of hot baths" (Prichard, 1841, Vol. III, 341).

The Laplander, on the other hand, never keeps himself in a degree of temperature sufficient for the full development of physical life.

Prichard has obviously leaned heavily on Scheffer and Blumenbach for he quoted from both of them *in extenso*. His results differ only to the extent of reinterpreting the mechanism of environmental causation. Although the conception of moral conditions as opposed to local conditions is attributed to Von Buch, one cannot help wondering if concern with this problem did not find its stimulus in the dissention of William Lawrence.

In 1859 Theodor Waitz stated that the Finns have short conical crania with flat temples and a globular occiput. The Lapps differ in that their skulls are smaller and thinner (Waitz, 1863, 76).

The Lapps and the Finns are held to be members of the same race. This conclusion is apparently based mainly on linguistic evidence. Indeed, language was considered important enough to permit the statement that, "We do not consider that the linguist is justified in conceding so much in this respect to the anatomist and zoologist as Pott has done, who assumes that intermixture has produced an essential change in physical formation among the Magyars, Osmanlis, Finns, and Samojeds, while they have preserved their language—that 'an exchange of body' with foreign tribes has taken place without an exchange of soul..." (Waitz, 1863, 76–7).

Waitz contended, "One is certainly inclined to doubt the theory of the absolute permanence of types, and to adopt rather an extensive change in the form of the crania by climate and intellectual pursuits" (Waitz, 1863, 76). The Finns were formerly free owners of the soil and their monuments and their poetry testify of a high culture in past times. The Lapps, on the other hand, have always been, and still are, "miserable nomads." "Might not the physical differences be considered as having gradually arisen?" According to Waitz, many consider shape of cranium an infallible criterion of race, yet experts admit that the individual differences in form of the cranium become greater in proportion to the higher intellectual development of a nation. He therefore concluded that the pretended constancy of physical type as a criterion of affinity of race results in absurdities (Waitz, 1863, 77, 226).

Waitz considered the Finns, the Lapps, and the Samoyeds members of the same race. He apparently also believed that they were related to the Mongolians for he held that large groups of Samoyeds in the south indicates their origin from Central Asia (Waitz, 1863, 199).

According to Anders Retzius (1860) there are two great racial groups, (1) the Dolichocephalae, and (2) the Brachycephalae, which are subdivided into (a) the Orthognathous, and (b) the Prognathae (Retzius, 1860, 251).

Among the Brachycephalae-Orthognathic of Europe are

the Ougriens and the Turks. The former include the Samoyeds, Laplanders, and Finns. Among the Brachycephalae-Orthognathic of Asia are the Ugrians and the Turks again (the difference in spelling has no apparent significance). The former includes specifically the Samoyeds and the Yakouts (Retzius, 1860, 257).

In this highly schematized outline based simply on a comparison of cephalic index and facial projection the old idea that the Lapps, Finns, and Asiatics are related is presented once again.

In 1886 A. H. Keane wrote twenty-two pages about the Lapps under the title, "The Lapps: Their Origin, Ethnical Affinities, Physical and Mental Characteristics, Usages, Present Status, and Future Prospects." From this article we learn,

notwithstanding many discrepancies due partly to long isolation in different surrounds, partly to intermixture, the Lapps would appear to be an offshoot of the great Finno-Tataric (Uralo-Altaic) family. . . . To this widespread division of the Asiatic world they still belong in speech and in some prominent physical characteristics (Keane, 1886, 217–8).

The Lappish language is a near relation to Finnish, which is closely allied to the Turki and other members of the Mongolo-Tatar group (Keane, 1886, 218). In fact, the name *Finn* indicates the connection of the Lapps with the Finnish family, of which they are evidentally an outlying branch, and it is moreover the Teutonic translation of the national name *Same*, e.g., literally, Fen Man (Keane, 1886, 215).

There is, however, more than purely linguistic evidence for the oriental extraction of the Lapps. In their national legends dim traditions still linger of their Eastern origin and their name connects them with Finland as the last stage in their long wanderings from the Altai and Baikal regions.

In their myths and folklore occur descriptions which can refer only to the Altai highlands, and Lake Baikal itself seems to be here indicated as a sort of point of dispersion for the Lapp race . . . (Keane, 1886, 217).

Physically, Keane felt that the Lapps are fundamentally, and in some respects even typically, Mongolic. They are not only brachycephalic, they are hyperbrachycephalic; they are not only short, they are extremely short. Yet, their hair is brown when it should be black; their complexion is florid when it should be yellowish; their eyes are brown when they should be black; and their nose is straight and regular when it should be short and concave (Keane, 1886, 219). These peculiarities are difficult to account for. They could be due to natural evolution of type gradually brought about during long seclusion in a changed environment. On the other hand, "we are warned by Linné not to attach too much weight to the element of color, which, amongst other races also is far from constant, and which appears to be peculiarly susceptible to climatic and dietary influences (Keane, 1886, 219). Other influences besides change of scene must have been at work, however, and the most important of these would have been intermingling of races (Keane, 1886, 220).

Keane has undoubtedly been both directly and indirectly influenced by the grand old man of Lappology, Scheffer. This is evident not only from some of the data used, especially the linguistic arguments, but also in his description of the Lapps as strong, of robust constitution, with good muscular development, but bandy-legged and ungainly walkers (Keane, 1886, 220).

The Races of Man written by J. Deniker in 1889 was based on the principle that race requires only a consideration of physical characters (Deniker, 1901, 280 f.). Under *Group F.*, *Straight Hair*, the following peoples were included (Deniker, 1901, 286).

warm yellow skin		⎰ N. American 22
		⎱ C. American 23
		⎩ Patagonian 24
brownish-yellow skin, etc.		Eskimo 25
yellowish white skin	a. turned-up nose, short stature, brachyceph.	Lapp 26
	b. St. or concave nose, short, meso- or dolicocephalic, projecting cheek bones.	Ugrian 27
	c. St. nose, med. stature, hyperbrachyceph.	Turko-tatar 28
pale yellow skin, etc.		Mongol 29

In this outline the Lapps are obviously related to the Mongols, as are also the Ugrians. But what is included under the term Ugrian? For Retzius, as we have seen, it comprised Samoyeds, Laplanders, and Finns. To de Quatrefages, on the other hand, it meant Samoyeds but NOT Finns. (Quatrefages, 1867, 513). A hint as to Deniker's interpretation is gained from a later article (1897) where he speaks of the Finno-Ugrians as Eastern Finnish (Deniker, 1897, 298). Apparently Deniker recognized more than one kind of Finn and did not connect the Lapps promiscuously with the Finns as a whole.

In 1899 William Z. Ripley wrote,

the Lapps . . . are among the broadest-headed of men. Their squat faces show it. In Stature they are among the shortest of the human species. . . . Their hair and eyes are very dark brown, often black. *Could any type of human beings be further removed from this than the Finns?* (Ripley, 1899, 359). (The italics are mine.)

If Deniker adumbrated the collapse of a time-worn theory it became a reality with Ripley. In the final moments of the 19th century the belief that the Finns and the Lapps were racially related was delivered a blow from which it never was to recover.

With Ripley and the turn of the century, then, the theory was abandoned that the Lapps were related to the Finns and represented a European extension of the Mongoloid race. If the preceding pages have given the impression that this was the only theory current until the 20th century then let that impression be corrected now. As early as 1684 F. Bernier classified man into four races: (1) white, (2) yellow, (3) black, and (4) Laplanders, thus recognizing the Lapps as a distinct race (Cf. Bendyshe, 1863/64, 360). In 1826 Lehrberg maintained that the Lapps and Finns were entirely different races, based chiefly on the argument that there were moral and physical diversities between them (Lehrberg, 1826). As early as 1850 Agassiz put the Lapps in a circum-polar race called hyperborean, (Cf. Nott and Gliddon, 1860, lxi) as did such later authors as Giuffrida-Ruggeri and de Lapouge, giving the group such respectable names as homo palaeoarcticus and homo hyperboreus (Manker, 1947, 39).

But, even though other theories existed, the fact still remains that in the 17th, 18th, and 19th centuries one interpretation of the racial history of the Lapps was supported by most outstanding physical anthropologists. The interpretation postulated a relationship of Lapp, Finn, and Mongoloid that was in fact unproven. Evidence for this myth, as shown, included a variety of explanations by different authorities. Occasionally, investigators accepted a predecessor's version of the myth, but for contrary rather than simply different reasons. In all events, the theory survived this long period of time as a kind of tradition. Handed down from person to person and from generation to generation, it found its chief support in the prestige and stability that comes from association with great names and respectable age.

A Modern Interpretation

The theory of Lapp racial origins that became a 20th-century tradition was first presented by C. H. Stratz in 1904. According to Stratz, the Lapps represent the last remains of a particular branch of a white-yellow ur-race. The Lapps are characterized by the presence of "individual protomorphic symptoms," e.g., long arms and short legs, a decided accentuation of the torus frontalis, and a decidedly high but wide nose (Kajava, 1927, 41). These "individual protomorphic symptoms," together with the lack of the "outstandingly individual, one-sidedly progressive characteristics" of the yellow and white races indicate the possibility that the Lapps represent a "protomorphic remnant" of the "*weissgelben Urstamm*" (Cf. Kajava, 1927, 41).

The investigations of Lassila published in 1921 were taken to support this view, since he demonstrated additional primitive characteristics of the skull (especially on the orbits) and the teeth (Cf. Manker, 1947, 40).

Writing in 1927, the Finnish scientist Yrjö Kajava found that his researches also supported this hypothesis, since he too noted certain "protomorphic peculiarities," such as the proportions of the trunk and the extremities, the low cranial capacity, the width of the nose, and the narrowness of the Fissura orbitalis inferior (Kajava, 1927, 41).

A moment's reflection is sufficient to indicate that the evidence used by Stratz, Lassila, and Kajava is so inconclusive that it renders any historical deductions absurd. Even if we were to grant the tenuous proposition that relatively short legs are a primitive survival, it is difficult to agree that the cranial capacity of the Lapps (1398.9 cc.) compared to the average European figure (1450 cc.) is small, especially in view of their short stature, which these writers do not suggest is a primitive characteristic. Indeed, Kajava's figures show the average female Lapp to have a cranial capacity of 1300.87 as compared to an average female European capacity of 1300 (Kajava, 1927, 41). Neither can the width of the nose be taken as primitive, especially since it is, according to Stratz, combined with a decidedly high bridge, which must be regarded as a progresisve trait. Indeed, of the three or four primitive characteristics cited by Stratz and Kajava, the nose is more than an unreasonable inclusion, it is detrimental to the whole hypothesis, for the nose of the Lapps, having considerable height, approaches the Caucasian, ergo progressive, type more closely than the extremely low, wide Mongoloid type. How then can it be held that the Lapps represent a remnant of the ur-race that developed into both the yellow and the white races! Surely not on the indefensible grounds that they lack the "individually outstanding, one-sidedly progressive characteristics" that are found in the Mongoloid and Caucasian races. Nor, again, because of the retention of dubious primitive characteristics. Yet, in the final analysis, this hypothesis rests precisely on the assumption, supposedly proven, that the Lapps are both primitive and unspecialized. Because they are primitive they represent a survival (protomorph) of an older racial type, and because they are simple, they represent the racial type from which the more specialized Mongoloids and Caucasoids developed. As we have seen, the evidence for simplicity and primitivity do not hold up even on the basis of their own data. Furthermore, even if they were primitive, Kajava's environmental deductions would suggest that it is the result of degeneration rather than survival. And even if they were simple, why should they represent the ur-race from which the white and the yellow races both developed?

The ur-race theory was the result of unwarranted interpretations of physical characteristics and unreasonable deductions on the basis of these unwarranted interpretations. Yet the tradition survived.

H. Bryn, a Norwegian, writing between 1920 and 1934, noted in a southern province of Norway (Møre) a population characterized by short stature. He felt that this group was so distinct from the typical Nordic type that it must originally have had approximately the same racial features as the Lapps, including marked brachycephaly, originally black hair and brown eyes. He found this element especially in the southern part of the province (Søndmøre) where the absence of mountain passes had hindered Nordic infiltration (Wiklund, 1947, 5–6). In a later report (1933–4) he referred to this group as "the dark, brachycephalic, high-headed type, which has its radial center in Sunnfjord" (5 or 6 miles south of Søndmøre) (Wiklund, 1947, 6). He noted again its geographical isolation and held that it belonged to the area of expansion of Fosna culture.

Bryn is of the opinion that this type, as well as the brachycephalic population of Jaeren (south of Stavanger in southern Norway), points towards the Alps in Central Europe. The high headedness of the Sunnfjord and Søndmøre population is due, in his opinion, to a later crossing of the Alpine type with the Nordic high-headed Trønder-type (Wiklund, 1947, 6).

He denied the existence of any Mongoloid characteristics in the Lapps and held that the contention of Stratz that the Lapps were a Mongoloid protomorph was "a completely untenable theory" (Schreiner, 1935, 286–7). This would appear to be only a partial acceptance of the Stratz-Kajava hypothesis. Actually, he believed that the Lapps must have had their origin far back in antiquity, before the formation of the Central Asiatic differentiation. Bryn's theory, then, is only a modification necessitated by his belief that Mongoloid characters do not occur among the Lapps. Stated succinctly, he considered the Lapps to be a derivative of an ancient Alpine race that broke away before the differentiation of the Central Asiatic type.

J. Czekanowski, writing at about the same time as Bryn, presented the thesis that there were four basic white races and six sub-races or mixed types (Wiklund, 1947, 15–6). These four races were the Lapponoid, Nordic, Ibero-Insular, and Armenoid. Defining Lapponoid in such a way as to include the Alpine and the Lapp proper, Czekanowski's conclusions agree substantially with Bryn.

Von Eickstedt, following the lead of Bryn and Czekanowski, also identifies the Lapps with an old European racial type. According to von Eickstedt, an extra-primitive proto-Alpine type went to Denmark to associate itself with the Maglemose culture. Later, under pressure from the advancing Nordics, these brachycephals were forced back until they were allowed to rest at the termini of the two Nordic routes of invasion (Coon, 1939, 287). These peoples, called proto-Alpines, are regarded as pure descendants of the early racial type of the Alps, "and not as an alpinoid, short-headed variant in the north" (Cf. Schreiner, 1935, 278).

Now, it is clear that Bryn, Czekanowski, and von Eickstedt have only partially accepted the hypothesis of Stratz, Lassila, and Kajava. Insofar as the most tenuous contention of the earlier writers was the assumption that early Mongoloids and early Lapps stemmed from a common race, it would appear that the later writers have accepted only the more reasonable premises. Such, however, is not the case, for, while they all agree in joining the Lapps and the Alpines, the premises on which this is based are completely different. As we have noted above, the earlier writers based their conclusions on an assumed primitiveness and simplicity in the Lapp physical type. The later writers, on the other hand, ignore this completely, and ground their deductions on a comparison of gross physical features as well as geographical and historical observations. It is indeed striking that this interpretation has had the same history as theories of preceding centuries: originally based on falacious data and reasoning, it has survived, through a process of reexamination and the support of different evidence and arguments. The belief that the proto-Mongoloids and proto-Lapps were related was dismissed by Bryn on the grounds that no Asiatic traits are observable in the Lapps, and by von Eickstedt on the grounds that such traits exist but are the result of later influences. The tradition, however, did not succumb. It was resurrected *in toto* by K. E. Schreiner in 1935.

Working with skeletal material, Schreiner observed that, "by combination and accentuation of several of these characteristics the Lapps, especially the women and children, can present a very singular Mongolian-like appearance . . ." (Schreiner, 1935, 277). On the other hand, there are many individuals among the Lapps who are not markedly Mongolian in appearance, but resemble certain elements in the southern part of Norway. "These types belong to a round-headed population of dark complexion which, with Ripley, we are accustomed to regard as a branch of the Central European or Alpine race" (Schreiner, 1935, 277). Still others look like an Alpine-Nordic mixture; but this is obviously due to recent intermarriage.

Schreiner noted, from a comparison of the cranial characteristics of Mongolians, Alpines, and Lapps, that in a large number of features, the Lapp skulls take a medium position between the other two, although there are also Lapp characters which are closer to either the one or the other and there are even some that typify the Lapps alone. His conclusion is, ". . . that the proto-Lapps, proto-Alpines, and proto-Mongolians, just as Stratz conjectured, represent differentiations of a common Ur-race . . ." (Schreiner, 1935, 287). While the proto-Alpines pressed to the west and the proto-Mongolians pressed to the east, the proto-Lapps moved into the area of the Urals, where they developed their specializations in isolation, before migrating to the Scandinavian peninsula (Schreiner, 1935, 287).

Although admittedly supporting the Stratz hypothesis completely, it should be noted that Schreiner found certain specializations in Lapp osteology which would render the Stratz argument nugatory. In basing the proto-Lapp, proto-Alpine connection instead mainly on an assumed connection between the Lapps and the southern Norwegian brachycephals, and hence the Alpines, he is clearly following Bryn, Czekanowski, and von Eickstedt in detail. He took issue with these men on the other half of the Stratz hypothesis. He demonstrated from his craniological research that Bryn's denial of the existence of Mongoloid characteristics in the Lapp racial type was incorrect. Von Eickstedt's contention that these Asiatic traits were due to recent admixture was countered mainly by the argument that the Lapps, who are in many ways less specialized than the Mongoloids, take up a position craniologically between the Mongolians and the Alpines.

C. S. Coon (1939) presented his analysis with considerable detail and specificity; yet, from what we have seen of the tenacity of racial interpretations, it is hardly surprising that he ends up essentially with the Stratz hypothesis:

Lappish: A stunted, highly brachycephalized, largely brunet relative of the Ladogan, originally living to the east of the Ladogan type area, in the Urals and Western Siberia. Has probably assimilated some evolved Mongoloid, but owes its partly Mongoloid appearance more to the retention of an early intermediate evolutionary condition. In modern times much mixed with Ladogan and Nordic (Coon, 1939, 292).

Schreiner's position reappears in Coon's terminology. Thus, the original ancestral Lapps are accepted as representing a stage in the evolution of both the Upper Palaeolithic Europeans and the Mongoloids, and that while the Mongoloids have specialized in their own characteristic way, and while the Ice-Age European strain was modified by mixture with and virtual absorbtion by the encroaching post-Pleistocene food producers, the ancestral Lapps were modified largely by a general size reduction and an increasing infantilism (Coon, 1939, 305).

Concerning the more recent racial history of the Lapps, Coon referred to the effect of an hypothesized process of brachycephalization, and to "Some environmental mechanism working upon the mineral economy of this peripheral human group [which] has probably produced this size reduction and infantilism" (Coon, 1939, 305). It is interesting to note that in spite of its sophisticated phraseology and the fact that it may yet be proven correct, the latter is precisely the explanation of short stature used by many of the earlier writers discussed above, including Blumenbach in the 18th century and Scheffer in the 17th. Even when Scheffer applied this environmental argument it was blessed with authority, for he quoted Vostius and Paulus Jovius.

From anthropometrical data Coon concluded that peculiar specializations, including characteristics of the jaw and the bony orbit, indicate a divergence of the Lapps from the Upper Palaeolithic Whites and the Mongoloids as early as the Laufen glacial retreat (Coon, 1939, 305). The lack of specialization in a Mongoloid direction, evidenced by the soft and often fine head hair, the absence of the blue-black hair pigment shade, the infrequency of the Mongoloid eyefold, and the absence of an excessive lateral malar development or great facial width, indicate that the Mongoloid characters of the Lapps could not have resulted from recent crossings.

In 1947 K. B. Wiklund's *Lapperne* was published posthumously. According to this outstanding Swedish Lappologist, "the numerous primitive characteristics of the Lapps possibly find their explanation in that they represent a protomorph— a remnant preserved to this day of the root from which the white and the yellow races had their origin" (Wiklund, 1947, 4).

Wiklund's debt to Stratz is obvious, for he not only has a footnote reference to *Naturgeschichte des Menschen,* but for the first time since Kajava in 1925 the old argument based on primitive characteristics is used.

Following Bryn and Schreiner, Wiklund holds that the Lapps are related to the Søndmøre brachycephals of the south Norwegian coast and thus ultimately to the central European Alpines (Wiklund, 1947, 5–6).

Following Schreiner he believes that the specializations of the Lapps must have required a long separation from the ur-race. "The peculiar anthropological type of the Lapps must have developed within an isolated area that was a strong barrier to contract with other peoples" (Wiklund, 1947, 6). He considers it a possibility that the Stone Age cultures of Møre and Sunnfjord, where there are present day peoples strongly reminiscent of the Lapps, are related to Fosna and perhaps to Komsa, which he believes dates from the last interglacial. Thus, while he agrees with Coon that certain peculiarities of Lapp physical type necessitate the assumption of the lapse of a long period of time since their connection with the Alpines and Mongoloids, he regards Komsa as possible evidence of their isolation in northern Fennoscandia, while Coon ignores Komsa and believes them only recently pushed into the Arctic and hence, by his reasoning, a branch of the ur-race rather than local shrunken-palaeolithic-survivors.

Conclusion

In the preceding pages we have examined the two most prominent theories concerning the racial status of the Lapps in order to ascertain the extent to which subjective factors entered into interpretive analysis. It was demonstrated that the earlier theory was accepted by a considerable number of men during the course of three centuries, just as the later theory has had wide currency since the beginning of the 20th century. Since it was also clearly shown in both cases that different men attained the same theoretical results for completely different reasons—the reasons of predecessors often being ignored, denied, or contradicted—the conclusion is inescapable that subjective influences have been highly effective—even to the extent of overshadowing the influence of anthropometrical and logical analysis.

By the same token, however, one of the main findings of this study is reassuring, for it appears that hardly any theorist (most of whom, it must be remembered, were dealing with the Lapps only incidentally to much more comprehensive problems) accepted uncritically the conclusions of their predecessors in the way that the results of investigators are accepted categorically by the lay public. On the contrary, each one, though arriving at the same conclusion, did so as a rule on the basis of a restatement of the evidence, and even on the basis of completely different evidence.

This is reassuring, because notable progress is apparent in the acquisition and utilization of evidence. Thus, one of the main sources of error in older works was the confusion of cultural and physical phenomena. The earlier reliance on language for the determination of racial affinities is a classic example of this confusion, and the avoidance of this source of error by later racial biologists must be recognized as an important step forward. Another significant improvement in evidence is based on the improvement of descriptive techniques which has resulted in more reliable information and improved grounds for comparison.

Yet, although improvements in evidence are notable, they did not develop as fast as might have been hoped. Thus, seventeen years after the development by Retzius of the cephalic index, Waitz described the Lapp skull on the basis of unguided observation, and in the 1930's, although the cephalic index as a descriptive technique had been joined by additional measures, such as the height-length index, one might even then have wondered if in describing Lapp, Søndmøre, Alpine, and Mongoloid crania as brachycephalic one was actually dealing with truly comparable characters, or whether these are basically different kinds of brachycephaly; for it was clear then that the cephalic index is a gross descriptive device that ignores such important factors as the relation of the brain itself to the supraorbital ridges and the thickness of the occipital and parietal bones. Perhaps conscious effort to objectivity could reduce such lag.

This study of Lapp racial classifications, however, is not to be taken as an indictment of scientific procedure. Today, as physical anthropology has entered a new phase, gene pools and population dynamics are replacing races as foci of study. But these modern developments derived from dissatisfaction with older concepts, and thus owe their existence to them. Old theories—whether based upon intuition, common sense, authority, or inadequate research concepts and techniques— undoubtedly had to be explored before new ones could be developed. In this sense, scientific myths were useful. Usually, in fact, they were also recognized for what they were: tentative hypotheses. When they were not so recognized, they lulled theory-builders into wasteful speculation or diversion to other problems. A far more serious consequence threatens the unwary, however. In the search for guides to action, current tentative hypotheses may be utilized, especially by non-specialists, as bases for pragmatic decision. In this day when scientists are entering precipitously into world council chambers, the history of Lapp racial classification reminds us anew that even venerable conclusions or the opinions of experts may be no more than scientific myths, perhaps useful in the development of ideas, but irresponsible bases for policy or administration.

References

Blumenbach, J. F. 1865. *The Anthropological Treatises of J. F. Blumenbach*. Thomas Bendyshe, ed. London, Longman, Green, Longman, Roberts, and Green.

Coon, C. S. 1939. *The Races of Europe*. New York, Macmillan Co.

Deniker, J. 1901. *The Races of Man*. London, Walter Scott Ltd.

——— 1897. "Les Races Européennes (2e Communication Preliminaire)." *Bulletins de la Soc. d'Anthropologie de Paris*, Vol. 8, Series 4, pp. 291–301.

Kajava, Yrjö. 1925. "Beiträge zur Kenntnis der Rasseneigenschaften der Lappen." *Suomalainen tiedeakatemis*, Ser. A, 25.

Keane, A. H. 1886. "The Lapps: Their Origin, Ethnical Affinities, Physical and Mental Characteristics, Usages, Present Status, and Future Prospects." *R. J. A. I.*, Vol. XV, pp. 213–235.

Lawrence, Sir William. 1822. *Lectures on Physiology, Zoology, and the Natural History of Man*. London, Benbow.

Manker, Ernst. 1947. *De Svenska Fjällapparna*. Stockholm, Svenska Turistföreningens Förlag.

Nott, J. C., and G. R. Gliddon. 1860. *Types of Mankind*. Philadelphia, Lippincott.

Prichard, J. C. 1841. *Researches into the Physical History of Mankind*, Vol. III, 4th ed. London, Sherwood, Gilbert and Piper.

Quatrefages, M. A. de. 1867. *Rapport sur les Progrès de l'Anthropologie*. Paris, Imprimerie Imperiale.

Retzius, Anders. 1860. Present state of ethnology in relation to the form of the human skull. Smithsonian Institution, *Annual Report*.

Ripley, William Z. 1899. *The Races of Europe*. London, K. Paul, Trench, Trubner.

Scheffer, J. 1701. *The History of Lapland*. London, T. Newborough.

Schreiner, K. E. 1935. "Zur Osteologi der Lappen." *Institutet for Sammenlignende Kulturforskning*, Ser. B, Skrifter, XVIII, 1–2.

Bendyshe, Thomas. 1863/64. "The History of Anthropology." *Memoirs Read Before The Anthropological Society of London*, Vol. 1, pp. 360–364.

Waitz, Theodor. 1863. *Introduction to Anthropology*. London, Longman, Green, Longman, and Roberts.

Wiklund, K. B. 1947. *Lapperne*. (Nordisk Kultur No. 10.) Stockholm: A. Bonnier.

VI   The Race Concept

LANCELOT HOGBEN F.R.S.

In any sense in which the term *race* is intelligible to a biologist, it signifies a group which preserves more or less clear-cut characteristics within the framework of a wider assemblage of inter-fertile forms as the outcome of mutation pressure or selection in circumstances of geographical isolation or inbreeding imposed by human interference. All the available evidence about so mobile a species as *Homo sapiens* points to a long history of migrations in which very few assemblages of genotypes have remained in isolation long enough to ensure a high measure of homogeneity; and nothing we have learned during the past century about the geographical distribution of human physique has any certain relevance to the diversity of Man's unequally distributed cultural achievements. That a concept which has accordingly so exiguous a bearing on the contemporary distribution of the species has been the focus of so much unprofitable controversy would indeed be an enigma, if the peculiar circumstances incidental to the revival of evolutionary speculation in the mid-nineteenth century gave us no clue to the intellectual preoccupa-

"The Race Concept" by Lancelot Hogben, from *Man, Race and Darwin* ed. by Philip Mason, published by Oxford University Press for the Institute of Race Relations, 1960, pp. 11-23. Reprinted by permission.

tions of a period during which it emerged into prominence after the publication of Darwin's *Origin of Species*.

In recent times, physique has equipped few men more felicitously than Charles Darwin and Karl Marx to fulfil the role of father figure. Devoted followers of each have fathered on them views which they could not possibly have entertained in their lifetimes unless endowed with second sight. Such has been the destiny of many others, notably Newton; but judicious appraisal of Newton's contributions in his own generation did not arouse passions which a discussion of the views of Marx still excites, and those of Darwin, at least till lately, excited. Happily, one can now re-examine Darwin's credentials before an audience that attained intellectual maturity after the controversy over his teaching had begun to cool off.

To get the major issues sharply into focus, certain facts about the material circumstances and mental climate of Darwin's time are highly relevant. Of the former, three are most significant. During the thirty years before *The Origin of Species* appeared:

(*a*) oceanic navigation under steam power had both greatly enlarged opportunities for a global survey of living beings and forced the problems of geographical distribution on the attention of naturalists:

(*b*) surveying of the type initiated during the period of canal construction had received a new impetus from railway construction;

(*c*) optical technology had borne fruit in cardinal improvements both of the microscope and of the telescope.

The first of these signalized the acquisition of a heretofore undiscussed body of data challenging, if only because of their novelty, to traditional views concerning the origin of the contemporary diversity of animal and plant life. The second had equipped the collector of fossils with contour maps confirmatory of the general picture of the formation of the earth's crust first advanced by Hutton in the context of a precocious outburst of evolutionary speculation to which Erasmus, the grandfather of Charles Darwin, had contributed. Before 1810, there was little or no basis for anticipation of rational grounds for presuming an orderly succession of new types throughout a period of time vastly greater than the duration of the written record of human existence. By 1860, the principle of geological succession was a commonplace.

In the same milieu, advances of optical technology are revealing in a different sense. In its own setting, the microscope which accompanied Darwin on the *Beagle* was not despicable, though by modern standards fitting only as a Christmas gift for an eleven-year plus. Darwin himself was about twenty years old when the newer microscopes bore fruit in Amici's discovery that one pollen grain fertilizes one ovule, and when Cuvier assigned the human sperm as a parasitic organism to the genus Cercaria in his *Règne Animal*. The reproductive processes of Cryptogams then justified their designation. That few zoologists in 1850 accepted the doctrine that one animal sperm fertilizes one ovum sufficiently explains why no zoologists—including Darwin and Wallace—recognized the wider implications of Mendel's work published nine years after the reading of their joint communication. Modern methods of fixation began to come into use during the fifties; but there were as yet no microtomes which could take advantage of the fact. The numerical constancy of the chromosomes was unrecognized. Indeed, Hertwig and Fol gave the first ocular demonstration that only one sperm fertilizes one ovum some fifteen years after *The Origin of Species* appeared; and the date is especially eloquent because any intelligible meaning we now attach to the term biparental inheritance in a biological context is referable to the material contribution of the sperm and the ovum to the outcome of the developmental process.

The three material features of the setting for the revival of evolutionary speculation at the end of the sixth decade of the nineteenth century have special interest if we also recall that it happened at a time when three major controversies dominated the ideological scene:

(*a*) Well into Darwin's manhood, well-nigh all the English leaders of natural science, Faraday and Joule like Davy, Henry, Dalton and Priestley before them, being non-conformists, had no university training. The Godless College of Gower Street was nonexistent in Darwin's boyhood, and a Test Act excluded nonconformists from Cambridge till ten years, Oxford till twenty years, after the *Origin* appeared. Till the latter date, and throughout nearly the whole of Darwin's lifetime, the claims of ecclesiastical and secular authorities to control the educational system at every level were the focus of bitter controversy.

(*b*) The repeal of the Corn Laws occurred twelve years before the celebrated joint communication, and throughout the greater period of Darwin's lifetime the notion of free competition as a social ethic was a focus of secular controversy debated with scarcely less vehemence than the right of the Bishop's bench to censor a curriculum of naturalistic studies.

(*c*) Darwin could recall the abolition of the British slave trade during his boyhood, and had started his professional career as a naturalist in the Royal Navy before the prohibition of slave ownership in the British Colonies. The abolition controversy was at its height during the decade which ended with the appearance of the *Origin*. The American Civil War began within four years of this event, and each side had vehement supporters in Britain.

With the end in view and with the space at my disposal, it is not possible to dovetail all these clues to the impace of the *Origin* on his contemporaries. So I shall say no more about the relevance of the *laissez faire* controversy to the peculiar appeal of the Malthusian jingle in the disillusion subsequent to the bright hopes of the French physiocrats. Nor shall I deal with the comic irrelevance of Herbert Spencer's beatification of natural selection as the Survival of the Fittest. None the less, we cannot judiciously assess the effect of Darwin's teaching on the discussion of racial questions, if we regard the issues involved as exclusively factual or logical. Biologists of the mid-nineteenth century approached them with social preoccupations intelligible only in the context of abolition and with views about the bearing of geographical varieties in general on the evolutionary problem intelligible only in the context of theological debate. Indeed a brief digression on the Test Act situation in its own technological setting will usefully emphasize how exiguous were the logical ties between what Darwin asserted and contemporary interpretation of his teaching, the more so because the *Origin* evoked no controversy conducted with comparable vehemence in contemporary France, where men of science in the tradition of the *Ecole Polytechnique* were mostly *libres penseurs*.

In its own social context, we have seen that technological advances had made possible considerable advances of scientific knowledge contributory to a formidable body of geological and geographical data which a Biblical view of creation, upholstered by Paley's natural theology with a teleological rationale, could not readily coordinate in a framework satisfactory to a sceptic. In the same milieu as the Test Act controversy, the untimely intervention of Bishop Wilberforce against so astute a champion of debate as Thomas Henry Huxley at the British Association of 1860 set what was to be the pattern of a contest which proceeded for more than a genera-

tion within the framework of common acceptance of a stupendous *non sequitur*. Thenceforth, both contestants subscribed to the dual proposition: if Darwin and Wallace are
right, Genesis is wrong, and if Genesis is wrong, Darwin and
Wallace are right.

The first half of the proposition is unexceptionable, and
the second is silly unless we concede that there are only two
conceivable accounts of the origin of the diversity of living
beings. It is therefore essential to remind ourselves that evolution is not the bare statement subsumed in the factual assertion
embodied in the historic principle of geological succession. The
doctrine of evolution makes the *additional* assertion that the
divergent succession of living types is a consequence of the
two circumstances incidental to the normal process of generation now subsumed by the terms hereditary transmission and
genetic variation. In fact, as earlier remarks on the role of the
microscope have sufficiently emphasized, it was not possible at
that time to formulate clearly what we mean by the distinction
and it was wholly impossible therefore to produce experimental evidence in support of the addendum.

Doubtless Darwin, who discreetly kept in the background
of what was essentially an ideological controversy little to his
taste, sensed this deficiency. At least, he followed up his mas-
terly assemblage of facts invitatory to speculation on origins at
a new level of discussion by publishing an anthology of domestic varieties of animals. For two reasons, we can say in
retrospect without hesitation that *Animals and Plants under
Domestication* adds nothing conclusive to the debate from a
scientific, in contradistinction to an ideological, viewpoint.
One is that most, if not all, of the data are susceptible to the
interpretation that new domesticated varieties have arisen by
recombination of highly diversified gene complexes through
crossing different inter-fertile local varieties; and the possibility of change through such a process in the absence of muta-

tion terminates automatically when we have extracted all viable recombinations. The other circumstance that deprives the argument of cogency depends on whether we define species in terms of what botanists sometimes respectively call Linnaean and Jordanian species. The latter include inter-fertile geographical varieties, but the former include units which either produce sterile offspring or no offspring at all when mated *inter se*. Darwin's data with respect to animals and plants under domestication throw no light whatever on how bisexual forms can arise, if inter-sterile with parent stock in this sense.

Only during the last half century have we gained conclusive proof of the mutation process and only in our generation have we obtained clear-cut evidence that new forms inter-sterile with parent stock can arise without supernatural intervention. Otherwise, as recognized by Philip (the father of Edmund) Gosse, himself a professional geologist, we are free to interpret the historical record of the rocks as an indefinitely protracted sequence of acts on the part of a suppositious creator. As a devout Plymouth Brother, Philip Gosse conceived the time scale of the sequence to be commensurate with the majesty of Jehovah with full scriptural authority for the assertion that a day is with the Lord as a thousand years. On this understanding, anyone with a flair for the esoteric use of language can accommodate the facts as then known with a poetic interpretation of the Pentateuch narrative.

Such vagueness of the species concept as Darwin's zoological contemporaries used the term casts a long shadow over the discussion of inter-fertile local varieties of *Homo sapiens* in the ideological context of the abolition controversy. Taxonomists had not—and have not yet—resolved the antinomy of natural and artificial classification at the level discussed so informatively and inconclusively by Whewell in the first half of the nineteenth century. The popularity of evolution exonerated them from further discussion of the issue in terms of the adequacy or inadequacy of a traditional two-valued logic by endowing the task with a new and, as we now see, unattainable objective which condemned zoology to wander for forty years in a barren wilderness of phylogenetic speculation. In the exhilarating climate of emancipation from Paley's natural theology, transitional types whose intrusion into an otherwise tidy taxonomy had hitherto been a liability, had now the assurance of a cordial welcome as missing links. In short, Darwin's followers regarded the best arrangement of species within genera as an arrangement which mirrors phyletic relationships. By the same token, they equally condoned the propriety of discussing which inter-fertile local varieties within a species are more or less ancestral. Fortified by the belief that human fatigue is the only obstacle to the elucidation of such pedigrees by recourse to anatomical data, taxonomists undertook their self-consecrated heraldic task with no misgivings about the outcome.

Indeed, it will be difficult to believe that such a hope could have sustained such stupendous persistence in fruitless and trivial exploits of repetitive mensuration, if we do not fortify our credulity with the reflection that persons of considerable intellectual standing enthusiastically subscribed to the cult of phrenology when craniometry was still in the cradle. Even so, early measurements should have sufficed to damp the ardour of the most credulous craniometrician, if rational considerations had any relevance to the issue. The cranial capacity of Bismarck was 1,965 c.c. and his brain weighed 1,867 grams. The cranial capacity of Leibnitz, who advanced mathematics as few others of a very creative period, anticipated the study of comparative linguistics and managed the financial affairs of the Elector who founded the Hanoverian dynasty, was 1,422 c.c. and his estimated brainweight was 1,257 grams. The

figure for cranial capacity is instructive placed side by side
with the following means:

Buriats (Mongols)	1,496
Kaffirs	1,460
Eskimos	1,563
Amerindians	1,450
La Chapelle Man	1,620

How lately such considerations influenced discussion of
the geographical distribution of human endowments is evident
from an autopsy on an (at the time) widely quoted Carnegie
Institution publication by Davenport and Steggera (1930),
based on a study of 372 Jamaicans chromatically classified by
the authors as Blacks 105, Whites 100 and Browns 165. By that
time the I.Q. had come into the field as a serious competitor to
craniometrical precision. On the basis of samples not too size-
able to exorcize scrupulous attention to the method of social
selection employed, the authors arrive (*inter alia*) both at: (*a*)
the encouraging conclusion that Whites were "outstandingly
superior in their ability" to detect ridiculous conclusions, since
they did best in Tests No. III (answer to "common sense"
questions), No. IV (meaning of words) and No. V (recon-
struction of pied sentences); (*b*) the discomforting disclosure
that the Blacks excelled in Tests No. I (following complicated
directions), No. II (problems in mental arithmetic), No. VI
(recognizing and continuing numerical series) and No. VII
(logical relations and analogies). The authors adroitly talk
their way out of this dilemma by asserting (p. 469) that "the
Blacks seem to do better in simple arithmetic and with numerical series" because "it seems a plausible hypothesis for which
there is considerable support that the more complicated a
brain, the more numerous its association fibers, the less satisfactorily it performs the simple numerical problems which a

calculating machine does so quickly and accurately." It would be paranoid to attribute a mischievous intention to any whose criteria of reasoning are so sub-standard.

Both contemporary genetical considerations referable to repetitive and back-mutation at the same locus and palaeontogical evidence of the extent of convergence in the past, have now taught us to dismiss the possibility that we can ever hope to tailor the terminal twigs of a taxonomic system to a historical sequence; but the illusion that it is possible to do so was undoubtedly the midwife to the discipline we now call physical anthropology. Reference to the literature of the time abundantly discloses that one circumstance propitious to this was the hope of demonstrating that the African Negro is more primitive in a zoological sense than the Southern gentry and their supporters. Whence we are to conclude that the African is: (*a*) less teachable; (*b*) not entitled to use the ballot box; (*c*) a suitable beast of burden for the white man. Each of the last three statements is a *non sequitur*, though little recognized as such in the highly impassioned climate of debate at the time of the American Civil War and its aftermath. Today, it suffices to comment that the hope which sustained the undertaking is itself illusory.

A humane man, who expresses in his Journal profound disgust towards the institution of slave ownership, Darwin bears no responsibility for this perversion of his teaching. It is also relevant to recall that the *Origin* appeared before the publication of the microbiological researches of Koch and the immunological studies of Pasteur. Only during the last fifty years have parasitological investigations familiarized us with a host of data relevant to the question: what obstacles have retarded the technological development of the African peoples? Of itself, the fact that domesticable ungulates in general and the horse in particular are highly susceptible to trypanosomiasis has condemned Africans south of the Tropic of Cancer to be their own beasts of burden in territories where malaria,[1] yellow fever, hookworm, bilharzia and many other diseases only lately recognized by medical science exact a heavy toll from the vitality of the people.

In the highly charged emotional climate of the Test Act controversy, thinking about the race issue was liable to distortion for another reason, which Disraeli's memorable phrase recalls. Briefly, the uprisen ape was by no means a fallen angel. Provoked by the irrationalities of their opponents, biologists thus found themselves sorely tempted to justify the inclusion of Man in the animal kingdom by recourse to arguments more menacing to the credentials of their antagonists than relevant to the rationale of a taxonomical preference. Inevitably in the heat of debate, it seemed all-important to emphasize what Man shares with other animals, the more so because so much about Man's peculiarities still eludes what we ordinarily agree to call physiological inquiry.

To be sure, the new evangelists had good reason to believe that differences with respect to the genetic make-up of animal species are primarily responsible for differences of behaviour which distinguish one (e.g., a social ant) from another (e.g., a solitary bee). Thus the analogy between locally restricted species of social organisms with distinctive anatomical *facies* and human communities distinguishable both by different culture patterns and by minor somatic peculiarities such as of skin colour or hair, disposed of any embarrassing temptation to remedy lack of intensive study of what is peculiar to the human ecological system.

Nor need we blacken the good name of our illustrious forefathers for what should now seem to be rashness of judgment on such matters. Our situation is otherwise. No one with

---

1. One often hears from those who should know better that natural selection has made the African immune to malaria. In fact, malaria is a major menace of the African village in the early years of life.

educational pretensions still subscribes to Lightfoot's chronology, which dated the appearance of human life on this planet as September 12th, 3298 B.C., at 9 A.M. With Lightfoot, Ussher and Bishop Wilberforce so far in the rear, and with no less detachment than that with which our predecessors could examine what distinguishes the mussel or the marmot each as one animal species from all others, we ourselves ought now to be ready to ask: what distinguishes Man from other animal species? Admittedly, we have still far to go before we can comprehensively discuss in the language of physiology the characteristics which make Man unique; but we shall not fulfill our target requirements (if at all) unless we recognize what they are.

In broad terms, they are easy to state and commendably biological considerations do not discharge us from the obligation to do so. Man is uniquely educable. In a unique sense, Man is a tool-making organism. In a unique sense, Man is also an animal capable of *informative* communication through speech. Because of this threefold uniqueness, a single animal species can fashion a changing environment and hence a changing milieu for its own developmental process. Like any other organism, Man transmits his genes to the next generation; but for the three reasons stated, and in a sense which likewise transcends anything comparable that we may rightly say of any other species, Man also transmits experience to the next generation.

Thus every change of the human environment through human interference signalizes a new accretion of transmissible experience and a new potential of further change. Because of this, human society is a unique ecological system. It owes its essential peculiarities to idiosyncrasies on which the study of social Hymenoptera has little or no bearing. While there is admittedly a *prima facie* case for the assumption that other local differences of animal behaviour are finally traceable to differ-

ences within the proper province of genetics, there is no such
case for the presumption that different patterns of Man's
social behaviour are predominantly traceable to the same
source.

In the last resort, the mutation of chromosomes or of single
genes is admittedly the pace-maker of organic evolution. We
now know what the circumstances which determine its tempo
and character include. These are:

(a) the rate of mutation;
(b) the viability of mutant types *vis à vis* the immediately
    available environment or the secular changes of the
    latter;
(c) mating systems more or less propitious to the concen-
    tration of genotypes in pure lines in a particular eco-
    logical *niche*.

We also know, though only since 1920, that mutation rates
are highly variable. Consequently, the circumstance that many
species have remained in all detectable ways fixed throughout
vast geological epochs confronts our view of the evolutionary
panorama with no enigma. Darwin's contemporaries and immediate successors preferred to ignore it. More especially as
interpreted by Romanes and Galton after Weismann had dis-
credited the Lamarckian superstition, the exponents of Natural
Selection presented it as a process of ubiquitous, continuous
and uniform change. Accordingly, the possibility of social
change without concomitant organic change of comparable
magnitude seemed to be contrary to the Laws of Nature. On
the other hand, the possibility that *Homo sapiens* is a relatively
stagnant species from the genetic viewpoint is no-wise repug-
nant to what we now know as surely as we also know that the
human ecological system has a *momentum sui generis* regardless of concomitant selection of genotypes. No reasonable and

informed person doubts that human beings are genetically variable; but a rational examination of the relation of transmissible patterns of human behaviour both to the diversity of the external environment in time and space and to the systems of mating peculiar to local communities, must take within its scope a multi-dimensional potential of change attributable to the circumstance that one generation passes on to the next its own experience and the experience of its predecessors.

A single example should make this manifest. If the beginnings of civilization testify to the formative role of the calendar in the first stage of writing, they also disclose, and with equal eloquence, how latitude, climate and contour have been peculiarly propitious or otherwise to the universal necessity of time-keeping in communities which have refined the techniques or have failed to do so. Though we still know very little about the genetic endowments of human communities and most that we hear is suppositious, such manifest external circumstances favourable to cultural efflorescence and to cultural stagnation are manifold. Nor can we appreciate how vast a range of possibilities they endorse if we discuss them singly and in isolation from the sum of acquired experience on which a particular community can draw. When the migrations of human stocks bring them into contact with otherwise similar circumstances, it will rarely if ever happen that two communities will respond within a comparable framework of traditional behaviour and equipment. Whether new circumstances are favourable to human inventiveness or otherwise, and if favourable with what possible outcome, is an enigma which therefore subsumes vastly diverse admissible solutions.

Thus the interplay of the diversities of environment on the stock-in-trade of transmissible experience encompasses a wide range of possibilities *vis à vis* the tempo and character of social change. Indeed, the inertia of experience accumulated in dealing with a stimulus-complex which Toynbee calls the chal-

lenge of the environment may more or less effectively resist
the impulse to deal with a new stimulus in a new way when
other means of doing so are available. Accordingly, one may
cite numberless examples of how failure to take advantage of
a new situation may then deprive a community of the means
of meeting the challenge of a different and later situation. For
instance, the consequence of access to abundant root crops or
of migration into an area where domesticable ungulates are
available as beasts of burden may be quite different, if the
event follows, from what it will be if the same event antedates,
a well-established cereal economy. Equally, the adoption of a
maize rather than a millet economy may initiate a train of
events along a course with peculiarities—some medical—of
its own.

A little reflection on widely accessible and abundant
sources of information should therefore suffice to justify the
conclusion that the joint relation of the human personality to
its social and physical environment admits of many degrees of
freedom, that minor variations of the sequence of otherwise
similar stimuli may lead to widely divergent responses, and
that anticipation of future consequences from definitive ante-
cedents is rarely (if ever) a profitable undertaking. That the
human ecological system has unique features, that it has a
well-nigh limitless potential of change in the absence of the
operation of forces which make some animal and some plant
species more short-lived than others, and that genetic variability is never manifestly the pace-maker of such change are
indeed propositions attested by the proper study of mankind.
No knowledge we have yet gained from the study of plant or
animal breeding can nullify them. Accordingly, such knowledge is not necessarily relevant to the evaluation of the changing character of human society. It would be rash to deny the
possibility that genetic selection has played a part in the decline of civilizations, as asserted by R. A. Fisher and the late
unlamented Alfred Rosenburg; but it is reckless to assert that

it has done so without a searching examination of other possibilities, the more so when an assertion, itself perhaps plausibly relevant to a single instance, embraces the history of all civilizations.

Are we then to conclude that biology can make no contribution to the elucidation of circumstances contributory to the diversity of culture patterns more or less highly characteristic of human beings with predominant physical attributes in a particular locality in a particular epoch? Assuredly not, unless we concede the impertinent claim that genetics embraces the entire field of biological inquiry or subscribe to a still too widely current nineteenth-century attitude to technological progress in antiquity. In the first fine flush of an unprecedented sequence of inventions following the introduction of steam power and the elucidation of the electric current, it was easy for archaeologists to take an unduly teleological view of the origins of fire, implements, clothing, the calendar, writing and especially (as the term implies) the domestication of animals. If we dispense with the inclination to do so, we are free to regard advances of human technology during the greater part of the 25,000-year saga of our species as a succession of fortuitous blunders dictated by unforeseen circumstances. In so far as this may be true, the *Führerprinzip* drops out of the story as an irrelevant postulate.

We have then to re-examine from two points of view the meaning of what we have hitherto called domestication *vis à vis* the role of commensalism in the diversification of what I have here called the human ecological system, meaning thereby what biologists customarily mean in contradistinction to the parochial and restricted use of the term in the title of the Professor of Human Ecology in Cambridge University. The beginnings of this composite system of species relationships takes us back to the association of Man with inter-fertile local varieties of Canidae in the early Palaeolithic, and hence to the possibility of blundering into herdsmanship where:

(*a*) hunting nomads accompanied by their dogs came into contact with gregarious ungulates; (*b*) there were natural barriers to circumscribe an enclosure in which to round up a herd. From one viewpoint, we may therefore ask how the inclusion of one species in the ecological niche we call a local culture determines the subsequent inclusion of another. For instance, we may plausibly examine the sequence: given grain storage, then mice or rats, then the cat.

From a different viewpoint, we may ask: what new mechanical problems does the inclusion of a new species in the human ecological system force on the attention of the social group? For instance: is it a mere coincidence that the indigenous Americans, without horses when Europeans came to their continent, had not perfected the wheel? In *Habitat and Economy*, Daryll Forde has commendably put before us many problems of this type; but there is still considerable scope for fruitful co-operation between archaeologists, cultural anthropologists, zoologists and botanists in the search for answers to many others. In my view, we shall advance little towards a deeper understanding of the diversification of human culture patterns in space and time till we are able to answer them. To be sure, human ecology in the very restricted sense of the term, as used by the Medical Faculty of Cambridge, has its own role to play until we know far more than we know as yet about what obstacles to technological advance are attributable to harmful organisms as members of the human ecological system in the wider sense of the preceding discussion.

On the other hand, the time is long overdue to recognize that the Pearsonian discipline designated physical anthropology, conceived in any terms other than its relevance to stock-taking in the tailoring and furnishing trades, is a blind alley in the landscape of biological science, like its parent phrenology harmless as a hobby for the opulent aged, but with no rational claim to support from the public purse.

VII A Nonracial Approach Towards
the Understanding of
Human Diversity

C. LORING BRACE

It is the task of Physical Anthropology to further the understanding of human evolution. Of course the investigation and interpretation of the hominid fossil record is clearly one of the ways in which this is accomplished, but another and equally important approach is through the consideration of physical diversity among the living peoples of the world. Superficially it might seem as though it would be easier to deal with the abundant evidence present in the form of living peoples, but actually this turns out to be somewhat more difficult.

The paleoanthropologist's approach starts with the arranging of the known fossil record in time, after which the causal mechanisms postulated to produce the changes so observed can be discussed. To many, the analogous procedure on the part of the student of the living is to arrange the peoples of the world according to geographical location, and then to attempt an explanation for the population differences observed. In practice this is far less easy since a number of problems immediately arise which greatly complicate the issues.

First of all, it is extremely difficult to say where one population ends and another begins. An arrangement of world populations based on such characteristics as stature and head form would differ radically from an arrangement based on hair form and skin color. The criterion for the delineation of living human groups is considered to be their breeding behavior, and a population is then considered to be that group of people who habitually choose their mates from among themselves. This approach to the identification of meaningful human groups enjoys considerable following at the present time since, following the insights which have come from that branch of the biological sciences called population genetics, the unit which is significant for the evolutionary survival of a species has been recognized as the breeding population. This works quite well in delineating meaningful groups in nature such as, for instance, field mice or fruit flies. Zoologists have used the term "races" to designate breeding populations which share identifiable characteristics, and it has been assumed that a similar practice could be followed in dealing with human groups. When races are delineated for mankind by modern biologically oriented physical anthropologists, they are usually defined along these lines.

The use of such an approach as an attempt to discover biologically meaningful human groups usually does not take complete consideration of the fact that human breeding populations are determined by the dictates of culture, rather than by specifically physical features. Certainly the most valid groupings of human beings are based upon cultural criteria. This puts the physical anthropologist in the awkward position of having to base the analysis of human physical diversity upon groupings which are not primarily based upon morphological characteristics.

The result is that "race" has always been a troublesome issue for human biologists, aside from the social and political problems that have been involved. This accounts for the fact that there is such widespread disagreement among anthropologists concerning the definitions of race and the identification of the races of man. Definitions range all the way from the denial that races exist at all to the attempt to define race on an exclusively morphological basis, and, for the majority of anthropologists who recognize some division of *Homo sapiens* into constituent races, the number recognized has ranged all the way from two or three up into somewhere in the hundreds. Finally, once a given anthropologist has settled on a definition which suits him, he then discovers that there is relatively little that he can do with his races except to list them.

This is all in marked contrast to the convenience which the social scientist finds in the term race. While individual sociologists may hold slightly differing definitions, the differences are not significant and, in fact, disappear in practice. There is virtual unanimity among professionals in the applications and uses of the term. Even those anthropologists who have attempted to define race on biological grounds alone are forced to admit that the sociologist is quite properly within his own province when he studies the problems engendered by race relations. Obviously the concept of race is used in the same way by people concerned with a theoretical as well as an applied interest in politics, i.e., by political scientists as well as politicians.

The definition of race which is offered here is essentially that of the social scientist and is based upon the perception of physical traits which are assumed to characterize human groups. Race is defined as being:

a group of mankind, members of which can be identified by the possession of distinctive physical characteristics.

The inclusion of the word "distinctive" in this definition is crucial since the importance of race is primarily in human perception, and, of course, in the attitudes and actions of the perceivers. Unless differences are clearly and easily perceived, consistent attitudes and practices cannot be pursued, and the race in question loses its identity as far as the people under consideration and also the social scientists are concerned. In some cases, what are perceived as racial differences are in fact primarily cultural differences between people whose genetically based physical characteristics are not markedly distinguishable. For instance, if one were to send a Sikh man to a barber, give him a shave and a haircut, and dress him in a business suit, he would be indistinguishable from, say, someone of Italian or any other Mediterranean origin. The same thing would be true for a Sikh woman in, for instance, a bikini and a bathing cap. However, the man in beard and turban, and the woman in her sari are immediately recognizable as being racially distinct from people of European origin.

Because human breeding populations are delineated by culturally established boundaries, and because of the inhumanity which has been practiced in the name of race, it occasionally has been advocated that the term be entirely abandoned. In the past, certain authors (for instance Huxley 1941 [1926] and Montagu 1951) have noted that since culture determines the criteria by which human groups are delimited, the proper unit to be considered in discussing human breeding populations is the "ethnic group," and that the term race be given up for these purposes.

On the face of it, it might seem that race as it has been defined above, being breeding populations with the addition of perceived physical differences, would be the most desirable grouping for the exploration of human physical differences. Actually, as was perceived some time ago and recently re-emphasized (Hogben 1931; Huxley and Haddon 1936; Montagu 1941; Livingstone 1962), neither the use of breeding population (ethnic group) nor race, no matter how it is defined, is sufficient for the understanding of human diversity. It has become apparent that the assumption that there is something significant in the association of traits in a single group of people is an assumption which obscures the factors influencing the occurrence and distribution of any single trait. *The most important thing for the analysis of human variation is the appreciation of the selective pressures which have operated to influence the expression of each trait separately.* Since in many important cases the crucial selective factors have no reference to ethnic or population boundaries, obviously an approach which takes population as its unit for study will fail to produce an understanding of whatever is influencing the distribution of the characteristics in question.

At this point it should be noted that the biggest changes in the human fossil record occurred as a result of changes in the selective pressures affecting particular features, and the changes in the selective pressures in turn followed improvements in the primary adaptive mechanisms in question (Brace 1964). Since the primary human adaptive mechanism is culture, it may be legitimately asked why a culturally defined group should not be the proper unit for the study of adaptively determined human variation. The answer is that for some purposes the presence or absence of the crucial adaptation may indeed coincide with culturally determined population boundaries, but for most characteristics, the adaptations, while cultural, are quite unrestricted by the boundaries of specific cultures. For instance, metal cutting utensils are as much the property of the Congolese pygmy as they are the property of the Viennese or the Roman or the New Yorker. Clearly, many adaptively important cultural features are not limited by the boundaries of specific cultures, any more than are the genetic characteristics of particular populations limited by their preferred but not exclusively practiced breeding habits.

Human physical variation can best be understood by relating the distributions of specific morphological features to the distribution and history (also the prehistory) of the relevant selective and adaptive forces. In the section which follows, a few of the most obvious characteristics of mankind will be discussed where the distribution parallels the known or postulated distribution of the selective factors involved. Because of the stress which has been placed on characteristics controlled by single genes, it has been assumed by many recent authorities that only the study of such traits could produce any precise insight into human diversity. It is apparent, however, that most of the traits by which human races can be easily recognized are not single gene traits, and yet, as we shall see, their distribution is just as logical as that of the traits which are relatively simpler in their genetic background.

The traits which will be considered first are those which have been traditionally most important for racial recognition (or discrimination, depending on the purpose behind making the distinction). The first such trait which will be examined is skin color.

Skin Color

Figures 1a and 1b show the probable distribution of skin color throughout the world just before European exploration and colonization so radically changed human distributions on the face of the earth. It can be seen that dark pigmentation is found only among people who live within fifteen to twenty degrees of the equator, although not all people who live in the tropics are dark. Furthermore, some people who are generally

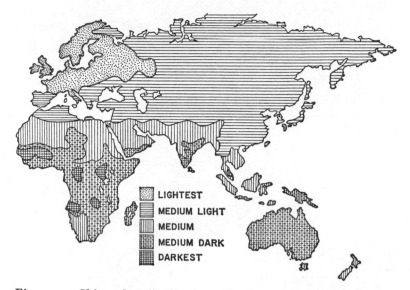

Figure 1a. Skin color distribution. Condensed and redrawn after Biasutti 1959. Old World.

accounted as being very dark may be partially exhibiting the effects of heavy sun tanning. The aboriginal inhabitants of Australia—particularly those who did not live in the extreme northern part—frequently bear testimony to the fact that their dark color is sometimes due to living out in the sun without any clothing.

In some areas, however, it is clear that people living within twenty degrees of the equator are definitely not noticeably dark, as is the case with the inhabitants of Indonesia and northern South America. In these cases, the people in question apparently have not been there for a sufficient period of time to have developed pigmentary protection.

The pigment in the human skin is a complex organic molecule called melanin. Its exact function is still a matter of dispute (Baker 1958), and, as with many of the other physical

Figure 1b. Skin color distribution. Condensed and redrawn after Biasutti 1959. New World.

differences between men, its importance is based on presumptive rather than proven evidence, but the presumptions appear reasonable and must be given thoughtful attention.

Where the ultraviolet component of solar radiation is strong, as it is in the tropics, the possibility of damage to the living cells in the dermis of the human skin is always present. Melanin in the outer layer of skin absorbs the harmful ultraviolet radiation and does not allow it to penetrate the living skin. As a result, physicians have long noted the much higher frequency of tissue injury and resultant skin cancer in relatively depigmented as opposed to relatively heavily pigmented peoples where the skin of both has been subjected to excessive amounts of sunshine (Keith 1949). Apparently dark skin has survival value in the tropics as people have suspected for many years.

Against this it has been argued that many dark-skinned tropic dwellers do not in fact have to contend with much strong sunlight. The Congo negro or the pygmy of the Ituri forest spend large parts of their lives sheltered by jungle, and yet they are quite well endowed with melanin. The answer is that neither of these people has been there for very long. While this at first seems unexpected in view of the widespread certainty that the Negro comes from the jungles of Africa, yet it turns out that this certainty is largely a piece of modern folklore. For one thing, the tropical rainforest is relatively restricted in extent, covering far less area than either dry grassland with scattered scrub trees or full desert. For another thing, survival in the rainforest depends on the possession of iron tools and suitable jungle-adapted crops, both of which are relatively recent in Africa. Apparently the Congo area has only recently sustained the populations which now live there, and a consideration of the selective pressures which were important in determining the skin color of the Congolese inhabitants at the present and in the recent past must look instead to the areas from which these people came. There are no historic records placing their origins, but linguistic and cultural evidence all indicates that they came from the area where the grassland merges with the forest to the north and west of the Congo basin and just south of 20° north latitude. The assumption that dark skin has value for people who have been adapting for a long time to an environment characterized by an abundance of tropical sunlight is not contradicted by the inhabitants of Africa, despite their present distribution.

While the equator passes several degrees south of the southernmost parts of India and Ceylon, yet the whole southern half of the Indian subcontinent from Bombay on down is below the twentieth parallel, and one would expect if our assumptions are correct, that the peoples who have inhabited these regions for the longest period of time, and hence who have been longest exposed to the selective effects of the environment, would show the greatest amount of pigmentation in their skins. As is expected, the peoples whom present cultural and linguistic evidence suggest were the most ancient inhabitants of the area are indeed the darkest in color (this is supported by the myths, legends, semihistorical and historical writings of the ancient Aryans). For instance, the Munda speaking people, as relatively northerly outposts in central India, but most particularly back-woods "hill tribes" such as the Kadar of southern India and the Vedda of Ceylon. In general, there is a north-south color gradient with the darkest people in the south. India, then, supports the generalizations which have been made on the basis of skin color distribution in Africa.

In southeast Asia, Indonesia, and the western Pacific again the initial impression is one of a great confusion of different colors. The equator runs right through the middle of the big islands of Sumatra and Borneo, just south of the tip of the Malay peninsula, and just north of New Guinea, and the area bracketed by 20° N and 20° S, includes mainland Southeast Asia, the northern quarter of Australia, and all of the islands in between extending far east into the Polynesian part of the Pacific. There are no really dark-skinned people in Sumatra or Borneo or the parts of Indonesia right on the equator, and it is not until one gets farther away from mainland southeast Asia, such as into parts of the Philippines, New Guinea,

Melanesia, and northern Australia, that one finds the kind of really dark brown skin which for purposes of social discrimination is called black. A few peoples in the refuge of the Malay jungles and the inhabitants of the out-of-the-way Andaman Islands, between the Malay peninsula and India, also show very dark skins, but with these exceptions the bulk of the people in Indonesia and southeast Asia range from brown in the south to yellow-brown up near the Chinese border.

The reason why there is so little evidence for dark skin among the inhabitants of the western and northern parts of this area is tied up with the history of population movements during the recent past. On the basis of the remnant peoples such as the Semang and Sakai of the Malay peninsula, the Andaman islanders, the Aeta of the Philippines and other less adequate hints, it is reasonable to regard the original inhabitants of the whole area as having been dark. Population was not dense because the basic means of subsistence was hunting and gathering which requires large areas to support limited numbers of people. The development of efficient farming techniques farther north allowed these northern peoples to spread south into what must have been for them relatively unoccupied country, absorbing and/or eliminating the few darker people who had formerly had the country to themselves.

Historical records amply confirm the north-south movements of the last 2000 years, and the decrease in both cultural and physical resemblances to the mainland becomes more marked the farther east one goes, until one reaches New Guinea. For a variety of reasons, the inhabitants of New Guinea and Australia are clearly the most ancient people of the area under consideration and consistently have dark skins. It seems reasonable to regard the Polynesians, who now spread far to the east of New Guinea, as being the end product of the

first great push from mainland southeast Asia, having passed
north of New Guinea itself. If we are correct in regarding
the whole area as having been thinly populated with dark
skinned peoples before the migrations, then the present remains of the first light skinned people to come from the mainland should show the effects of having absorbed darker elements on the way. This certainly is supported by the appearance of the present Polynesians.

In our consideration of the distribution of the various
shades of human pigmentation, no mention has been made of
the western hemisphere. In general, it appears that the Indians
had not been across the Bering Straits for a long enough time
for selection to have had much effect on skin color, even in
the most tropic parts of Central and South America. The color
of the Indians then, like that of the Indonesians, betrays their
eastern Asiatic origin.

So far, this presentation has been concerned with light
skinned people moving down into tropic areas where dark
people had prevailed. Of course, in Africa the formidable
barrier of the Sahara desert and the swamps of the upper Nile
prevented any such population movements, and in the New
World there were no preceding dark tropic dwellers, but this
picture holds true for Arabia, India, and Southeast Asia-
Indonesia. This southern expansion of light colored peoples
has been recognized by many generations of geographers,
historians, and anthropologists, but very few have grappled
with the question of why it happened.

There are two basic problems involved. First, what made
these people light skinned in the first place, and second, why
did they press south. The problem of their southerly movement has been treated from time to time, but it will be de-
ferred here until after the discussion of the problem of depigmentation. Some authorities have simply assumed that "white"
was the original color for all mankind, although this still

evades the question of what adaptive advantage it must have conferred in order to have originally become established.

Another suggestion has been advanced claiming that the reduction in epidermal melanin allows more ultraviolet radiation to penetrate the skin and aid in the formation of vitamin D. This presumably is an advantage in those parts of the north temperate zone where year around cloud cover so reduces the available amount of sunshine that every bit absorbed is of value. This view runs into difficulty when one realizes that at the time of year when sunlight is at its rarest and weakest, the greatest amount of depigmented skin is securely covered with quantities of clothing. By the same token, the fur covered members of the animal world should all be showing the effects of a severe vitamin D deficiency.

The mention of clothing brings us to what appears to be the real source of the reduction in skin pigment which is so apparent in peoples whose remote origins were in the neighborhood of 50° north latitude. From the foregoing discussion it seems apparent that a relatively great amount of skin pigment has been of value to a hairless animal living in the sunnier parts of the tropics, and since the fossil record points to just this area as the remote home for all mankind, there is some basis to assume that the remote human ancestors were dark in color. This being the case, our problem is to understand how some eventually became light.

While there can be no proof for it, this is offered as the most likely means by which it happened. The archeological record shows that relatively successful and extensive human occupation of the north temperate zone as a permanent habitat did not occur until the last glaciation. During the previous glaciations, the onset of cold conditions had forced people back south, but by the end of the third interglacial, the technological facets of developing human culture had just reached the point where, with some refinement, they would allow people to adapt to the cold instead of having to flee it. People stayed in the north, then, taking abundant advantage of the quantities of big game which lived there.

The archeological record shows an abundance of scrapers appearing in Europe and the Middle East at the onset of the Würm glaciation, and this clearly shows an increasing preoccupation with the preparation of animal skins. Equally clearly the Neanderthals did not tramp through the snows in the loin cloth type of garment pictured in the standard cartoon. One of the things which allowed them to survive was the use of adequate clothing. Now for the first time man presented something besides his own skin to the outer world, which meant that the presence or absence of melanin no longer had any importance.

With the adaptive significance of melanin substantially reduced starting with the onset of the last glaciation approximately 70,000 years ago, the genetic background for melanin production was free to vary, and the inevitable result was that mutations detrimental to melanin production occurred. Since these were not selected against because of the reduction in importance of the protective function formerly played by melanin, such mutations accumulated in these populations with the eventual result that melanin ceased to be produced with the same efficiency. Thus the cultural factors which allowed human survival in the north temperate zone greatly reduced the survival value of a particular trait—pigmentation —and the resultant accumulation of random mutations meant that the trait was eventually reduced, a process which has been termed "the probable mutation effect" (Brace 1963).

The degree of human depigmentation, wherever it is found, should indicate the length of time and the extent to which skin pigment has been reduced as an adaptive feature. This is borne out by observation since the people with the palest coloring in the world today are those who can trace their ancestry back to the zone stretching from western through eastern Europe and on into southern Russia where the archeological record gives evidence that human survival depended on the use of clothing for a longer period of time than anywhere else in the world. It is tempting to suggest that perhaps this may also be related to the reason why peoples stemming from northern Europe have always been so stuffy about the idea of human nudity, but this is going a bit beyond the realm of physical anthropology.

It might be asked why the inhabitants of northern China (Manchuria) and Mongolia are not as light-skinned as the Europeans of the same latitude. The answer must be that they have not been there for quite so long, and their ancestors therefore were not dependent upon clothing for survival purposes for as far back in time. The archeological record does not provide the same kind of confirmation for this view as it does for the interpretation advanced for the West since the artifacts assignable to the early Würm are notably meager, although this is actually what one would expect if the area were not permanently inhabited at this time. The near absence of evidence for human habitation at this time in the northern parts of the far East (see Chang 1962) is in marked contrast to the abundance of Mousterian remains in the West and must indicate that the depigmentation process in Asia started substantially more recently.

Eventually the cultural mechanism was developed which allowed the inhabitants of eastern Asia to spread north, and which at the same time allowed for a reduction in their epidermal melanin. In this northward spread during the final stages of the Würm, they encountered the Bering Strait land bridge which then was up to 1300 miles wide (Haag 1962), and as a result, populated the Western Hemisphere. With this background, the depigmentation of the inhabitants of eastern Asia and the New World should have started at the same time, and it is no surprise to discover that they are now approximately the same color.

Only two areas of the world suggest that the south temperate zone was inhabited back into the Pleistocene for any length of time, one being south Africa and the other being the southern half of Australia. While neither area shows evidence that clothing was ever used to the extent where it would reduce the significance of extensive skin pigmentation, yet both areas are south of the tropics and the intensity of ultraviolet radiation is substantially reduced. We should expect that peoples who can be regarded as long-time inhabitants of these zones would show at least a partial reduction in pigmentation from the condition associated with the descendants of the ancient dwellers in the tropics proper, and this is indeed the case. The aborigines of the southern part of Australia are not so dark as the "blackfellow" in the north, and the South African Bushmen and Hottentots are lighter still, being a sort of yellow-brown which accords with the suspicion based on archeological evidence that they have inhabited the southernmost parts of Africa for a longer period of time than the aborigines have lived in southern Australia.

Having thus accounted for the forces which produced differences in human skin color, it is now appropriate to make brief mention of the reasons why the recent past has seen such extensive movements on the part of the relatively depigmented peoples south into India and southeast Asia. The explanation runs like this. The technological and cultural changes which allowed men to survive in the temperate latitudes during the cold of the last glaciation, and which led to their eventual depigmentation, started trends in cultural adaptation which culminated in the discovery of methods of controlling the food supply after the Pleistocene was over. The Neolithic revolution was a cultural development which was distinguished by the beginning of human efforts to control the propagation of plants and animals.

The success of this food producing way of life, in contrast to the previous hunting and gathering kind of existence, can be seen in the vast increase in numbers of the peoples whose cultural heritage stems from this source. The food producing revolution occurred earliest in the Middle East starting approximately 10,000 years ago (Flannery 1961), and before long the area had about as many people as the existing subsistence techniques could support. Cultural elaboration including the improvement of farming was one result, but another was the actual movement of populations into areas where existing farming techniques could be applied and where the indigenous population was too sparse to provide an obstacle. Climate was a limiting factor to the north, although technological advances eventually mitigated this, but to the south the opportunities for expansion were somewhat less restricted, and the result was the kind of color distributions which we can see in the world today.

Hair

The form and color of the hair of the head is often given an importance second only to skin color by those who feel impelled to make racial discriminations. The geographical distribution of hair follows the distribution of skin color without exception, and, in spite of the numerous individuals where the two appear to be unrelated, it is apparent that this is the one instance where what is regarded as two traits vary together for a biological reason. Pigment in hair itself has no particular significance, but hair is a structure derived from the

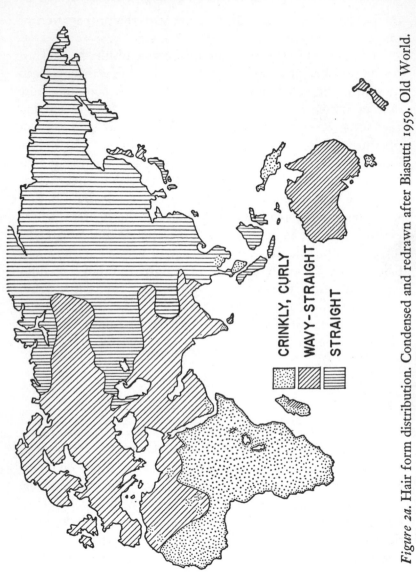

Figure 2a. Hair form distribution. Condensed and redrawn after Biasutti 1959. Old World.

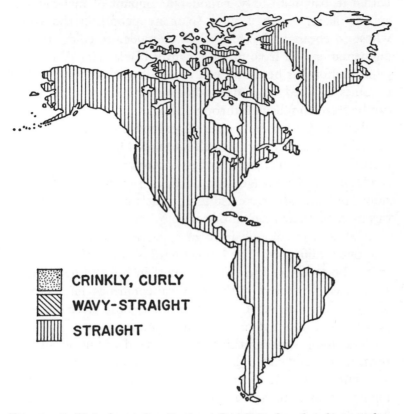

CRINKLY, CURLY
WAVY-STRAIGHT
STRAIGHT

Figure 2b. Hair form distribution. Condensed and redrawn after Biasutti 1959. New World.

epidermis and will necessarily share facets of the same system for melanin production.

For individuals whose forebears had become adapted to survival in areas of strong sunlight, the well developed melanin production system of the epidermis will certainly ensure that the hair too has its fair share of melanin. Because of the structure of hair and the arrangement of the melanin granules within it, hair with only a moderate amount of melanin will appear black, which is why so many people in the world whose forebears underwent slight to moderate epidermal depigmentation still have predominantly black hair. Where depigmentation has been allowed to become advanced, the hair becomes affected, and, depending on the degree, all shades can be seen from brown through blond.

Red hair is something else, the existence of red pigment in the skin and hair being not well accounted for as yet. It seems most likely, however, that redness in hair and skin arose as the result of random changes in a different part of the enzymatic substrate normally responsible for melanin production, but this must be accounted an educated guess.

Unlike hair color, hair form apparently has had definite adaptive significance. The human head is one of the few parts of the body where the skin is underlain by a rather thinner than usual protective cushion of subcutaneous fat. A good hair covering can serve as protection against mechanical injury to bone and that rather vital organ, the brain.

The most striking thing about the distribution of hair form is the tendency for the extremely kinky forms of hair to occur among the same people where the very darkest skin pigmentation is to be found. There is no direct correlation between skin color and hair form as is shown by the presence of the most extreme hair form among the only moderately pigmented Bushmen of South Africa, so the suspicion is raised that tightly spiral hair may be an adaptive feature, and the reason why its distribution parallels that of dark skin color is that both traits may be responses to related conditions. If dark skin is the adaptive response to high levels of ultraviolet radiation, and the insulation provided by woolly head hair is a response to high levels of solar heat radiation, then it is obvious that both adaptations are responses to different challenges evoked by living in an area characterized by an excessive amount of sunlight.

In the past, observers have noted the presence of dark skin and kinky hair in Africa, traces of it in southern Arabia, stronger traces among the hill tribes of India, the jungle peoples of the Malay Peninsula, the Andaman and Philippine pygmies, and finally its full development in the inhabitants of Melanesia, and have offered a number of theories involving vast migrations for obscure reasons. It is much easier, however, to regard these instances of the simultaneous occurrence of extremes of human variation in both skin color and hair form as the logical adaptive responses to similar selective pressures.

One more thing can be added in considering variations related to the hair. If our argument relating to depigmentation is generally applicable, then among those people who have provided cultural means for the protection of the head for the longest period of time, we should find the greatest amount of reduction in the biological adaptations normally associated with such protection. The same people who were the first to use clothing extensively may be assumed to have provided protection for the head, i.e., hats, and this assumption receives support from the fact that it is among their descendants today that we observe the highest proportion of deficiencies in the normal head protective mechanism—hair. Not surprisingly, it is among people of European derivation that the highest frequencies of gray hair and baldness occur.

So far, this discussion of human physical variation has dealt with extremes in adaptation which are responses to purely environmental selective forces. To be sure, these forces are limited by latitude instead of by specific geographic province or breeding population which means that no nice explanation can be offered which starts with the breeding population as the significant unit. The next facet of human variation to be considered also clearly shows the futility of starting one's analysis with "races" or breeding populations, since it cuts right across population and even geographic boundaries, again, as in the previous characteristic discussed, following the dictates of selection or its absence.

Face Form

Besides general pigmentation and hair form, the characteristics long considered of greatest importance for racial diagnosis are connected with the form of the face. While the previously discussed characteristics are not merely controlled by single genes or even by the various alleles of a single locus, yet they are genetically much simpler than the complex of anatomy which we call the face. Nevertheless, despite the complexities and unknowns which surround the genetic background of face form, an investigation of the variations in the human face shows that the differences can be associated with relatively clear differences in selective factors.

There are two aspects of the face each associated with a different major function subject to important differences in selective forces affecting human survival. These are the parts particularly associated with the respiratory passages and those associated with the whole chewing apparatus. It might be argued that the face is also the locus for the organs of sight which of course is true, but on the other hand the microscopic complexity of the visual machinery does not allow any gross anatomical differences to occur. Variations in the color of the eye, in color vision, visual acuity, and even in the size of the eyeball can occur without affecting the skeletal housing called the eye socket and without any influence on the anatomy of adjacent areas. This cannot be said for variations in the nose area and in the jaws and teeth, and it is the intent here to con-

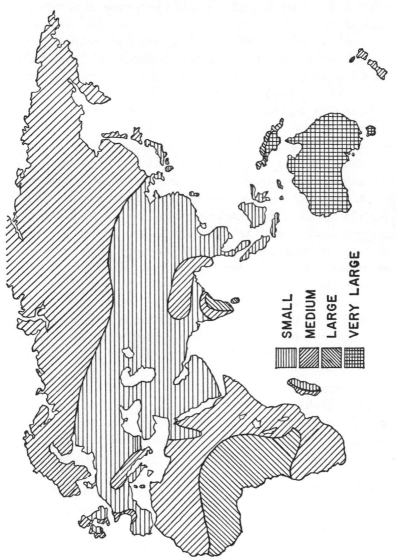

Figure 3. Face form distribution as indicated by relative tooth size.

sider such variations and the selective pressures which produce them.

Because variations in the dental apparatus are most clearly related to differences in selective pressures and because they have not been considered from this point of view previously, these will be considered first. Apart from the existence of an edge-to-edge bite in some peoples but not in others, which is partially but not entirely a matter of the characteristic mode of usage and hence wear, the primary differences in the human masticatory apparatus are simple differences in size. Some peoples have big teeth and some peoples have small teeth, and of course the whole tooth-bearing part of the face is related to the size of the teeth themselves. Not surprisingly, the people in whom the growth process produces large teeth also tend to have large jaws, large chewing muscles, and other evidences of exuberant bone growth associated with the skull and face.

Good studies on the dimensions of human teeth are surprisingly rare in scientific literature, but enough information is available to be able to arrive at a quite satisfactory understanding of the relationship between the size of the dentition and the selective factors influencing it. The smallest teeth are to be found among the peoples of Central and Eastern Europe and the Middle East, and the largest teeth are those of the Australian aborigines. Not only are Australian teeth the largest in the world, but under pre-European conditions they regularly showed the most extreme degree of wear (Campbell 1925).

This amount of abrasion points in a direct and simple manner to the selective forces operating to maintain large teeth. With the largest of human teeth being worn to the gums by middle age, it is easy to imagine what would happen if the teeth had been any smaller. Obviously, smaller teeth would wear down at an earlier age leaving the possessor effectively toothless in the prime of life. A toothless person in the Australian "outback" before the advent of European technology had a relatively reduced chance of surviving, and, if these circumstances occurred before the normal end of the reproductive life, the opportunities for transmitting the traits involving small tooth size to the next generation are materially decreased. The operation of the forces which maintained large teeth in pre-British Australia offers one of the clearest pictures of natural selection at work influencing human form and survival.

Since there are great differences in the amount of tooth wear to be seen among the different peoples of the world, and since extremes of tooth wear can influence the chances for survival, it is instructive to consider the causes for wear in its most pronounced form. Clearly the most important function of the masticatory apparatus is to reduce food to the appropriate form and size for swallowing. The teeth, as the bearing surfaces of this crushing machine, are worn, at least in part, by the abrasive content of the food they chew. In the case of the Australian aborigines, the game which they catch is singed by being rolled in the ashes of an open fire, briefly roasted, and then eaten—ashes, grit, and all—with a minimum of assistance from a manufactured cutlery. Of course the products of the hunt provide only a portion, and at that not even the major portion, of the aboriginal diet, although it was certainly large enough to account for a substantial amount of dental abrasion. The rest of the diet included varying amounts of seeds, nuts, fruits, berries, insects, roots and vegetable products most of which were eaten without any further preparation. Obviously the eating of the proverbial peck of dirt was an annual phenomenon for the Australian aborigines and not something which took a whole lifetime to accomplish.

While the immense variety of their diet might not qualify the Australians as a literal example of grinding poverty, yet there can be no question that such a regimen can produce a great deal of tooth wear. There is, however, another important source of tooth wear to be considered which has nothing to do with the diet, and this involves the observation, also made on other peoples who show similar kinds of tooth wear, that the aborigines use their mouths like a third hand. When first discovered, the Australian aborigines possessed a culture whose technological poverty was greater than that of any other people in the world, being on a par with what we believe the most advanced human technology was like some time during the third interglacial. With such a rudimentary tool kit, they frequently avail themselves of the convenient all-purpose tool which heredity had provided in the form of their large and powerful jaws and teeth. As vise, clamp, or pliers, the dentition is frequently used to hold objects which are then manipulated with the hands. The wear thus produced occurs in most pronounced form on the front teeth in contrast to wear produced by heavy duty food chewing which affects the molars, and it is interesting to note that it is the front teeth which show the most extreme degrees of wear by early middle age.

This being the case, one would expect an inverse correlation between the amount of wear on the front teeth and the level of technological development among the peoples of the world, and to a degree this holds true. The simplicity of the picture is somewhat spoiled by the discovery that a people such as the Eskimo, with a relatively complex technology for a nonliterate, nonindustrialized culture, show a quite similar degree of wear on the incisors, definitely limiting the chances for survival of the aging Eskimo. The special problems which survival in the Arctic raise mean that, despite the greater technological development, the Eskimo use their teeth extensively in manipulating their environment—untying knots, chewing frozen boots, and most important of all, tanning skins for clothing. Among most of the peoples of the world, however, the greater the technological complexity of their culture, the less the front teeth are worn and the smaller these teeth tend to be.

It is apparent that where the teeth are extensively used as tools, a premium is placed on large incisors. Small front teeth are distinctly disadvantageous and are actively selected against by the early deaths and failures of their possessors to reproduce. There is no problem, then, in explaining the existence of large teeth wherever they are found. The existence of small teeth at first seems somewhat less easy to account for, but a little reflection will show that their occurrence obeys the same principle which lies behind the distribution of depigmentation. Specifically, where technological development has resulted in the production of tools which are designed to perform the tasks formerly performed by the teeth, then the presence of large front teeth is no longer important for human survival. Random mutations affecting the teeth can occur without disadvantage, and since random mutation in reference to any structure eventually results in its reduction, the teeth in question are reduced (Brace 1963). As would be expected, the people with the smallest teeth in the world are those whose remote ancestors first developed a complex technology.

Technological complexity, however, is not limited by race, and, as a result, that part of face size which is contributed by the dentition varies across population boundaries in a way which would be quite inexplicable if racial group were taken as the starting point for analysis. Any chart attempting to trace the distribution of differences in human dentition size is plagued with two problems. First of all, published information exists for only a few human populations, and second, despite conflicting evidence (Garn and Lewis 1958), some correlation should exist between gross body size and tooth size. Figure 3 (page 125) is an admittedly subjective picture based on the available information crudely corrected for body size by showing the relative size of the teeth in proportion to body bulk. For instance, the Bushmen of South Africa have always been cited as having small teeth since their dimensions are approximately the same as those of Europeans, but then no consideration is taken of the fact that Bushmen are noticeably smaller in gross bulk. In proportion to their body size, Bushmen teeth are actually relatively large, although not in the same category as those of the Australian aborigines.

A few words of interpretation are in order for Figure 3. The smallest teeth belong to those people whose forebears first enjoyed the technological benefits made possible by the food producing revolution. Food producers with their sedentary existence generally accumulate more possessions and can therefore have a more elaborate technology than hunters and gatherers. Reasonably enough, then, there is a broad band extending from central Europe through the Middle East, across northern India into the Far East and Southeast Asia which corresponds with the areas where the food producing revolution had had its effects for the longest period of time.

Actually, plotting the distribution of relative gross tooth size in this manner obscures the fact that there is something of a West-East gradient in effective incisor size in the small tooth zone which is not expressed by simple length-width dimensions alone. This is due to a change in the form of the front teeth. Shovel-shaped incisors, dating from the observations of Hrdlička, 1920; 1921), have been assumed to characterize the inhabitants of eastern Asia, and, in an era when human morphological characteristics were assumed to have no functional significance, resemblances were supposed to indicate historic relationships between populations or races, and wherever shovel-shaped incisors were found, whether in American Indians or in Asiatic Pithecanthropines, it was presumed that this indicated some sort of relation to modern Asians. Re-examination of material found before the shovel shape was recognized as significant shows that not only the European Neanderthalers but also their Upper Paleolithic descendants had shovel-shaped incisors, although most modern Europeans do not.

The problem is less the explanation of the origin of shovel shaped teeth than explaining why they ceased to exist in the areas where they are now absent. Following the principle of trying to understand the reason for the existence of specific traits rather than taking the recognition of difference as being sufficiently important by itself, the significance of incisor form takes on a different aspect. Instead of being simply an indication of ancestry as it was formerly believed, the raised lingual margins of the incisors are an indication that the teeth were formerly (or still are) subjected to heavy usage and great wear. Adding to the total amount of incisor enamel by the raising of the lingual borders is a simple adaptive way in which the potential for wear is increased without the necessity of increasing overall tooth size and hence increasing jaw size (Brace 1962).

Although the evidence is not sufficient, it seems likely that all middle Pleistocene hominids had large shovel-shaped incisors. As technology developed and the value of large incisors decreased, particularly in that part of the temperate zone where the food-producing revolution took place, then the teeth were free to vary with the inevitable result that reduction occurred. There are two ways in which a shovel-shaped tooth can reduce, one is to reduce the overall dimensions which Figure 3 shows occurred all the way across the middle latitudes of the Old World. The other method of reduction is the elimination of the extra enamel in the form of the raised lingual margins. As a reflection of the fact that technological elaboration, in the form of Upper Paleolithic cultures and subsequently the earliest food producers, occurred earliest in the area from the Middle East through central

Europe, it is understandable why the absence of shovelling makes the effective amount of enamel less among the peoples of these areas then among the people farther east whose teeth are actually the same size in gross dimensions.

A comparison of the tooth dimension chart with that representing the distribution of variations in pigmentation shows that the two distributions do not correspond. In fact, starting in the Middle East where teeth are smallest and going north and west it can be seen that teeth actually increase in size while pigment decreases, with the largest teeth in Europe occurring at the extreme north and west fringes. Evidently while clothing was an ancient feature of cultural adaptation in these areas, the kind of technological complexity which goes with a food producing type of subsistence came much later—a statement which is supported by an abundance of archeological evidence.

The extent of a band of medium dentitions down the east part of Africa reflects the spread of effective stone cutting tools, of the sort which allowed the Neanderthal face to change into a more modern form, which occurred at about the same time that the Upper Paleolithic flourished in the north. This form of technological advance did not penetrate the edges of the forest region in West Africa and around the Congo basin—perhaps because of a lack of sufficient suitable raw materials—and the effect was that the dentitions of these peoples remained relatively larger. People with these larger teeth then multiplied in great quantities following the acquisition of farming techniques and suitable food crops which allowed them to spread into the previously unoccupied African rain forests. These people expanded to the south and east, spreading out into the area where only a moderately large lower face was characteristic, thus creating a somewhat confused picture for this trait in the southern parts of East African and the eastern parts of South Africa. The relative size of the lower part of the face in Africa evidently remains the same across boundaries of skin color, hair form, subsistence economy, and geographic province while at the same time varying within each of these. Clearly hair form or skin color or geographic province has no particular biological or adaptive tie with the size of the dentition so that any appraisal of human facial variations which starts with sociologically defined races as its basic units will fail to understand the distribution or the meaning of such variations. It is only by plotting the distribution along with that of the relevant selective factors that one can appreciate the problems involved.

Dental variation in the rest of the world follows the same principles. The parts of India and Southeast Asia in which remnants of hunting and gathering populations are to be found show a relative enlargement of the lower face. When New Guinea and Australia are added to the area considered, the results are just what one would expect, with the relative increase in face size showing a close correlation with the areas in which technological elaboration has been present for the shortest period of time.

Much less information is available for the Western Hemisphere so it has been left out of Figure 3, but every indication shows that it follows the same principles. Judging from photographs of Indians from all over both North and South America, it would appear that the smallest faces in the New World are confined to an area running from the highlands of Peru in western South America, north through Middle America to somewhere just south of the boundaries between Mexico and the United States. Reasonably enough, this corresponds with the area where food producing cultures have been in existence for the longest period of time in the Western Hemisphere.

The distribution of variations in the size of the human dental apparatus apparently follows the distribution of the relevant influencing factors in a reasonable fashion despite the sketchy nature of our information for many populations. Skin color also behaves in a similarly predictable manner, but the distribution of dental size bears no relation to that of skin color since the important influencing forces vary quite independently.

With two of the most outstanding characteristics by which people can be seen to vary evidently showing no relation to each other, it is not surprising to find that other areas of human variation which can be traced in terms of their influencing selective factors are also independent. While the shape of the lower part of the human face is determined by the development of the masticatory apparatus, variations in the upper face are dominated by the shape of the nose.

The history of human face form, starting with the pre-human ancestors of man and proceeding up to the present day, has been one of varying degrees of reduction. The dental apparatus has been greatly reduced as its defensive and manipulative functions have decreased, and the whole supporting facial skeleton has decreased along with it, with the exception of the part which has served as housing for the respiratory apparatus. Apparently it would have been detrimental to human survival to further reduce the air intake passages. The result has been the preservation of a relict of the former extent of facial development which we now identify as the human nose.

To a certain extent, then, the degree of nasal prominence is a reflection of the amount of reduction of the rest of the face. Part of nasal shape also is determined by the relative degree of development of the immediately adjacent parts of the face. For instance, the peoples who are noted for the possession of particularly broad noses all have particularly large incisors, meaning that the whole facial skeleton in the area where the nose is widest is noticeably spread. People such as the Australian aborigines and various other peoples from

New Guinea to western Africa where, for the reasons mentioned above, the incisors are particularly large evidently show a widening of the whole lower face including the external form of the nose.

In addition to the differences in the width of the lower part of the nose, there remain outstanding differences in the length of the nose and in the height of the nasal bridge which cannot simply be explained by citing different degrees of reduction in the rest of the face. The distribution of nose form in the world is shown in Figures 4a and 4b by the various values recorded for the nasal index. A low index indicates a long narrow nose while a high index describes a relatively short wide nose, but since, as we have seen, nasal width is at least partially accounted for by another trait which is distributed according to its own selective pressures, it is evident that the nasal index is not the best criterion of nasal length and height. It is the best measure available, however, and will have to serve as the basis for tentative interpretations.

Like dental size, the form of the nose does not correspond very closely to population boundaries, and, apart from the portion of its variation which is directly related to the size of the lower face, it appears that nose form responds to another set of influencing forces. A quick glance at Figures 4a and 4b will show that the relatively shortest noses occur only in the tropics, and observation confirms the fact that the nasal bridges of the peoples in question are low as well as being short. At first it seems as though no consistent sense could be made from such an observation since such people as the inhabitants of East Africa right on the equator have appreciably longer, narrower, and higher noses than the people in the Congo at the same latitude. A former generation of anthropologists used to explain this paradox by invoking an invasion by an itinerant "white" population from the Mediterranean area, although this solution raised more problems than it solved since the East Africans in question include some of the

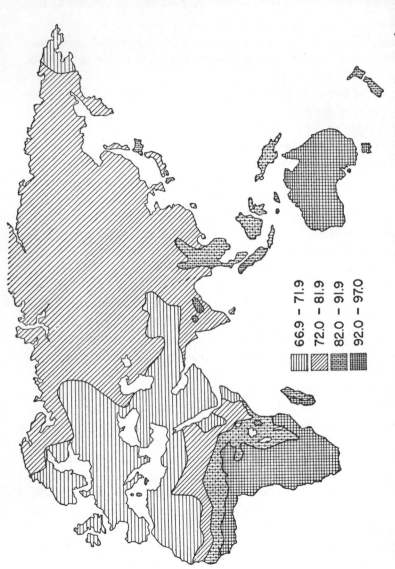

Figure 4a. Nose form distribution as seen in the nasal index. Condensed and redrawn after Biasutti 1959. Old World.

66.9 – 71.9
72.0 – 81.9
82.0 – 91.9
92.0 – 97.0

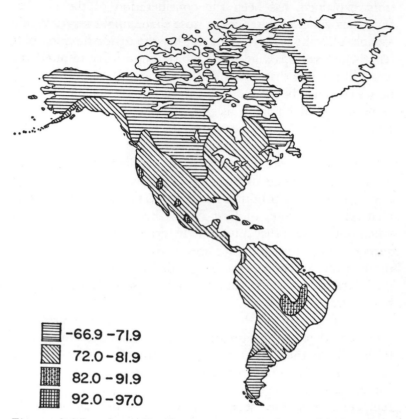

-66.9 -71.9
72.0 -81.9
82.0 -91.9
92.0 -97.0

Figure 4b. Nose form distribution as seen in the nasal index. Condensed and redrawn after Biasutti 1959. New World.

blackest people in the world with characteristically woolly hair and a body build unique among the world's populations for its extreme linearity and height.

While the full answer to nose form distribution is yet to be given, a good attempt supported by some significant research has been made (Weiner 1954). The point of departure, as with the other traits for which distributions have been sensibly explained, has been the consideration of the possible functions which differences in nose shape might serve. While Weiner's results seem to indicate that the major function of a lengthened nasal passage is the moistening of dry inspired air, it is still possible that a part of the significance of variation in nose shape may be related to the need to warm incoming air in extremely cold climates, as was suggested in earlier studies (Thomson and Buxton 1923; Davies 1932).

If there is merit to these suggestions the distribution of big noses should indicate the areas where people have had to cope with either extreme dryness or extreme cold, and by and large the actual distribution more or less fits expectations. The relatively long noses of East Africa become explicable then when one realizes that much of the area is extremely dry for parts of the year. The long noses of the dry Middle East and those of the cold northwest fringes of Europe fit expectations, but there are a number of cases which seem less obvious at first glance.

The Bushmen of the extremely dry Kalahari desert in southern Africa possess greatly reduced noses in seeming contradiction to their habitat. This becomes less of a paradox when it is realized that the Bushmen have only recently been forced to take refuge in the desert by the settlement of the temperate southernmost parts of Africa by peoples possessing more efficient subsistence techniques and weapons. Likewise, the inhabitants of the dry central Asiatic plains have only been there for the last few millennia. The Eskimo, too, can be viewed as a relative newcomer to the Arctic, and although they do indeed possess long narrow nasal passages, the nasal bridge is not so high as might be expected—perhaps in part due to the fact that the heavy stress put upon the dentition has meant that the rest of the face has undergone relatively less reduction than among the cold-adapted peoples of northern and western Europe.

The Australian aborigines are the final apparent exception to the presumed association of nasal length with lowered humidity. The Australian desert is one of the driest areas inhabited by man, yet the nasal index is relatively high. In this case, the actual length of the nose is over-shadowed by its great width, and this width is simply a reflection of the fact that the whole lower face is greatly broadened to accommodate the biggest incisors possessed by modern *Homo sapiens*. Within Australia itself, however, nose form varies in conjunction with humidity just as one would expect. The longest and highest noses occur in the central desert, while the shortest and lowest noses occur in the tropical and humid north.

A final comment on nose form concerns the explanation for the tendency for short low noses to occur among peoples who dwell in the humid parts of the tropics. This again appears to be a case of the reduction of a character which confers relatively little benefit on the possessors. Long nasal passages are of no particular advantage where the inspired air needs to be neither moistened nor warmed, and any variation arising in relation to nose form would be equally likely to survive. Since most naturally occurring variations will tend to reduce the size of the structure in question, the accumulation of their effects in time results in the reduction of the noses of the long-time denizens of the moist tropics.

Body Build

While the facets of morphology discussed above are those most commonly used in making racial distinctions, major differences have also been observed to occur in body build which make sense when considered in adaptive terms. Ob-

viously in a cold climate it is desirable to use the heat generated by metabolic activity as efficiently as possible. Conversely
it is equally apparent that for people to sustain activities in
very hot climates, the major concern is for the development of
some kind of mechanism which promotes the dissipation of the
heat generated in metabolising enough fuel to produce the activity in the first place. Since heat loss occurs at the surface of
the body, it is clear that bodies which have different relative
amounts of surface area will differ in the speed with which
heat dissipation occurs as a simple example demonstrates. If
one hundred pounds of copper is shaped into a sphere and
heated, it will hold its heat for a much longer period of time
than one hundred pounds of copper stretched out in a wire
a half mile long and heated to the same temperature. Not only
does shape influence the relationship between surface area
and bulk, but differences in gross size can also play a part.
Changes in surface area vary in proportion to the square of
linear dimensions while changes in volume vary as their cube,
so it is obvious that as the object in question gets bigger the
volume increases more rapidly than the surface area even
when the shape is held constant. Adaptive variations in both
size and shape have been recognized for man (Coon, Garn and
Birdsell 1950; Newman 1953).

Although there are many individual and group exceptions,
it can be said that, on the average, human bulk decreases in
the hotter and increases in the colder areas inhabited by man,
and the inference has been made that this is related to the
greater heat-conserving properties of larger bodies (Roberts
1953). But not only are there size differences, there are also
differences in shape. Long slender arms and legs are clearly
associated with desert-living peoples while short limbs and
heavy bodies can be seen in the arctic. A number of objections have been raised to considering the short limbs of arctic
peoples as adaptive, but it seems quite clear that the danger

of frostbite makes long arms and legs considerably less desirable in cold climates.

Against the adaptive value of specific body form in the tropics, it has been pointed out that the tallest as well as the smallest people in the world live very close to each other right on the equator in east central Africa. Actually, whether such a view is adequate or not, it can be argued that both extremes in body build are different ways of handling the heat dissipation problem. One way of presenting a maximum amount of surface area to the air is to stretch a given mass into an elongated shape, and certainly the immensely tall East Africans of the Upper Nile area are about as linear and elongated as people get. The other way of influencing the mass-surface area ratio is to change the size. Increasing gross size without changing form was seen to increase mass in proportion to surface area. This being true, the converse evidently is that a decrease in size will decrease the mass (proportional to the cube root of any linear dimension) in relation to the surface area thus accomplishing the same thing that shape modification can do.

The pygmy, simply by being small, acquires the same surface-mass ratio which is achieved by the Nilotic African who is normal in bulk but greatly elongated in shape. Since both are equally efficient heat dissipating mechanisms, the factors influencing which adaptation will occur stem from other sources than a simple concern for heat regulation. The tall East Africans generally are food producers whose subsistence is derived from their cattle. This means that the food supply is relatively assured and that they get regular amounts of protein in their diets. Pygmy subsistence, however, is less assured, and there may be long periods when food is not plentiful and little protein is eaten. This kind of problem would be particularly hard on people who are large enough so that they need a regular and substantial food intake, and of course, would be especially severe for the rapidly growing child. A people who have low nutritional requirements as adults and who grow less rapidly during the critical phases of development will have a better chance of surviving as marginal hunting and gathering populations in the fringes of tropical forests.

With small size being both efficient for heat dissipation and the best assurance for survival in an area afflicted with periodic nutritional bottlenecks, it becomes possible to understand why peoples within the pygmy stature range exist in such places as the eastern edge of the Congo basin, southern India and Ceylon, the Andaman Islands, Malaya, the Philippines, and the remote parts of New Guinea. With the limited amounts of big game in these areas and before the recent advent of iron tools and weapons in many of them, the survival value of being small is quite evident.

Former explanations for the distribution of pygmies relied on vast postulated migrations of a single stock of small-statured people throughout the tropics of the Old World, but it makes much better evolutionary sense simply to regard the pygmies, wherever they occur, as size adaptations made *in situ* by the local populations of the areas in question. The Congo pygmy is simply the small end and remnant of a distribution of hunting and gathering peoples which extended, prior to the diffusion of an agricultural subsistence base into sub-Saharan Africa, around the edges of the Congo forest and on through the edges of the West African forest where it merges with the savannah. In southern India, Ceylon, and Southeast Asia the peoples of pygmoid stature are the remnants of hunting and gathering populations which, because of the great southward push of food producing techniques and peoples into the more desirable areas, are confined to the more inaccessible and heavily forested refuges. Only in the Andaman Islands did pygmies remain unaffected by the unequal competition with food-producing peoples, although here the only choice for habitat was necessarily tropical forest with no big game and the same sort of occasional nutritional bottlenecks which plague hunting and gathering peoples in the tropical forests elsewhere.

For the reasons discussed under skin color and hair form, the remnants of the ancient inhabitants of southern India and Southeast Asia are all very dark in color and possess very tightly curled hair. In contrast to this, some of the jungle inhabitants of central Borneo and the Philippines have the reduced coloring and reduced hair curl which is more characteristic of the peoples who have arrived from the north in relatively recent times. At the same time, they are of extremely small size illustrating the selective effect which the problems of survival in such an environment exerts on the human physique regardless of the differences in other traits which may have developed in diverse geographical areas. In the highlands of New Guinea, as well, there are people of pygmy stature but, again, with very different faces from those of the short peoples of either Africa, Southeast Asia, or Borneo since they come closer to resembling smaller versions of the faces of the aborigines of Australia. Again, the effects of this kind of environment have determined the pygmy physique despite the differences in technological selective factors which have resulted in marked facial differences in the areas considered.

Central New Guinea is a particularly interesting case since there has been no overwhelming invasion by peoples whose characteristics developed in response to selective pressures elsewhere as was true for Southeast Asia and Indonesia, nor have new subsistence techniques been in effect for a long enough time for a substantial change in the distribution of local groups to have been distorted beyond the possibility of recognizing its original form, as has been the case in Africa. As a result, the New Guinea pygmy is not an abrupt isolated phenomenon, either culturally or physically, as is now general for the small peoples elsewhere in the world. Because New Guinea has been less overwhelmed either by invading peoples or by the effects of diffusing cultural features than anywhere else in the world, it is interesting to note that only here is there the completely gradual cline from the local normal sized peoples to the pygmies without break in just the manner which can be assumed to have once been the case for all the regions that now have isolated pygmy populations.

Before leaving the subject of the significance of variations in human physique, another set of influencing factors must be considered. While the pygmies appear to be a response to problems stemming from both periodic food shortages and the necessity for the efficient dissipation of metabolically generated heat, and other differences in physique appear to be adaptive, there seems to be another factor affecting human survival in parts of the temperate zone. A belt of chronic overpopulation and undernourishment extends from Egypt through India and into southern China and Southeast Asia, but the people, while small, have not become pygmoid in size. While it is impossible to do anything more than suggest the answer, it would appear that any further reduction in size would decrease the potential for the amount of labor which the people must sustain in order to survive. These people seem to be able to produce a maximum amount of work on the smallest possible number of calories per day. If they were larger, they would eat more than they could grow, and if they were smaller they could not sustain the amount of effort necessary to support a family, so a close adjustment is made, and, despite the different origins of the peoples in this belt, there is remarkable similarity in gross size and bodily proportions.

Enough has been said about the gross morphological variations visible in mankind. Others exist which have not been treated, and much of what has been said has been obvious but undocumented by the kind of solid proof which is usually demanded of biological interpretation. The object in presenting it has been not only to touch on the major observable variations in man, but also to demonstrate that the various traits in which people differ are distributed according to the selective factors responsible for their expression and not because of any association with socially delimited boundaries such as the perception of race. Where the selective factors are related or happen to vary together, then the traits they influence will likewise vary together, but, as has been shown, it is commoner to see the selective forces and their corresponding traits varying more or less independently of each other and crossing geographical and population boundaries without regard to the supposed limits of human gene pools or areas of mating preference.

Traits with Known Modes of Inheritance

If this approach to understanding human variation is clear when gross morphology is the subject for consideration, it is at least as obvious when characteristics are investigated for which a precise knowledge exists concerning the genetic background. In fact, in much recent biological thinking there has been the feeling that morphological variation is difficult to appraise since the precise mode of inheritance of morphology is so poorly known and the result has been the abandonment of morphology as a valid area for investigation by many recent students (see Livingstone 1961). This explains the reason why the data on which this present appraisal of human morphological variation is based was collected primarily a generation or more ago and remains so incomplete.

Within the last two to three decades there has been a belief among biologists and particularly biological anthropologists that the simple understanding of the genetics of a trait was sufficient reason for collecting information about the occurrence of the traits in question in many human populations. Consequently the energy which had gone into morphological trait gathering in generations gone by has been recently poured into genetic trait gathering. The result has been the collection of an enormous amount of information relating to human characteristics with a simple mode of inheritance. Recalling the role of the basic genetic material in the production of protein molecules (Crick 1958), it is not unexpected that many of the features which are inherited as single gene characters turn out to be proteins or closely related molecules (Harris 1959). Within the last few years, the realization has grown that the distribution of some of these traits corresponds with the distribution of recognized and important selective factors. Now at last some evolutionary sense can be made out of what formerly seemed to be merely biochemical oddities.

A significant attempt has been made in the interpretation of the distribution of deficiencies in color vision (Post 1962). While the exact biochemical deficiency which produces failures to see colors is unknown, the mode of inheritance is clear and simple. Contrary to popular assumptions, failure to see red and failure to see green are not due to the same genetic deficiency, although the genes controlling each type of vision occur at loci on the X chromosome and hence are examples of the phenomenon of ordinary genetic linkage as well as sex-linkage. While genetically these are actually two separate traits, yet as far as the individual possessing either is concerned, failure to see colors, whatever the genetic source, is subject to the same kind of selection, and, for purposes of distribution studies, there is some justification in lumping the two. Furthermore, many studies have failed to recognize the differences and have lumped them anyway. It seems obvious that visual acuity, including color vision ability, is highly desirable for a people depending on hunting and gathering as their chief mode of subsistence. Post has noted that any deficiency in vision among such a group should be detrimental and should be selected against. For people at a food producing level of subsistence, the penalties for poor color vision should be less severe, and one would expect mutations affecting vision to accumulate in time, eventually resulting in a reduction of visual efficiency in the same manner whereby skin pigmentation undergoes reduction following the suspension of the significant selective factors.

Theoretically, then, one would expect the highest percentage in deficiencies of color vision to occur among people whose forebears were the first to forsake a foraging for a food producing mode of subsistence, and therefore one would further expect the distribution of increasing color vision deficiency to correspond with the cline of dental reduction. The expectation is fulfilled in most instances with the highest percentages of colorblindness occurring among the peoples of European and Middle Eastern origin, followed closely by Chinese. This is reasonable since, as with the slightly lesser degree of dental reduction in Asia, the food producing revolution occurred slightly later in China than it did in the Middle East.

The lowest percentages of color vision deficiency occur among modern hunting and gathering populations, although there is some confusion in the evidence where the samples tested are too small to be reliable. Clearly, then, the distribution of colorblindness frequencies, in cutting across boundaries of socially perceived racial differences, behaves in the same manner that has already been demonstrated for morphological features. Again, the most important criterion to consider is the distribution of the selecting force.

One of the clearest cases of the relation between selective forces and the distribution of the associated trait has been pre-

sented in Livingstone's classic work on the distribution of abnormal hemoglobins (1958). This is too well known to be repeated here, although it should be noted that as a result of his
careful study, we now have a well documented picture of the
spread of a trait not only by actual population movement but
across population boundaries as a result of the inevitable genetic
exchange which adjacent populations practice. Since the
genetics of this trait are simple and the selective forces involved are so strong, it can be quantified in a way which is not
possible for the morphological traits which have previously
been discussed. Because of this, Hemoglobin S can serve as a
model for understanding the mechanisms behind the distribution of any trait whose expression is subject to natural selection in man, whether it be a single gene character or one controlled by an unknown number of genes and loci. Livingstone,
despite his reluctance to deal with trait distributions where
the mode of inheritance is not clear, has fully appreciated the
significance of his discoveries in the undermining of the standard anthropological use of the concept of race (Livingstone
1962, and as revised in the present volume pp. 46–60), and
his position would appear to be substantially the same as that
being advocated in this present paper.

With the insights gained from the successful interpretation
of the various facets of the abnormal hemoglobins, it is now
becoming possible to foresee the explanation of some other
characteristics which have been known but not understood for
quite some time. For instance, as long as human blood groups
were considered to be nonadaptive (Boyd 1950), it was impossible to make any sense out of their distributions. Because
of the clearly inherited nature of serological phenomena, they
were siezed upon with enthusiasm as the best racial markers
known. There were two consequences of this approach to the
study of human diversity. First, the fact that biologists started
with the assumption that racial groups (breeding populations)
were the significant units for analysis provided fuel to those

people who wished for their own profit to believe that human races are of different innate worth, hence justifying existing practices of racial discrimination. The second consequence was that by restricting consideration to breeding populations, it was difficult to appreciate the covariation of selective factors and the respective human adaptations where these crossed population boundaries as they do in so many cases. This means that a full understanding of human variation and how it arose was not possible.

Recently, however, there has been a change in the orientation of the people interested in human diversity. It has been realized that a simple naming of human groups or races has no particular significance as a biological aim, although the study of human group relations and hence group identification has real significance for the sociologist and for other social scientists. In addition, human biologists have increasingly realized that their primary task is the explanation of how human variations arose, and it is obvious that the assumption that human differences are nonadaptive defeats any such effort before it is begun. If man's form is the product of evolution, then man's differences must be evolutionary responses to different selective pressures, and it should be possible to explain differences in what were once considered the least adaptive of nonadaptive characters, the various blood types.

With this revitalized evolutionary view in mind, some effort has been made to discover what selective factors could account for the marked differences in allelic frequencies which A B O system exhibits in the various parts of the world. With the different alleles showing some association with disorders of the digestive system (gastric ulcer and intestinal carcinoma), suspicion has arisen that A B O differences may be related to characteristic differences in diet (Kelso and Armelagos 1962). With the immunological techniques, by which blood types are recognized, testing primarily for incompatibilities in closely related proteinoids, it seemed probable that the various blood types may have something to do with adjustments to other complex organic molecules which are frequently encountered during daily life—for instance in eating. The preliminary research of Kelso and Armelagos shows that there is indeed a suggestive association between various frequencies of the A B O system and major population differences in characteristic amounts of fat, carbohydrate, and protein intake. Further work may show that different kinds of protein may correspond to particular A B O frequencies—for example, some peoples derive most of their proteins from animals while others get the greater quantity from such vegetable foods as beans or lentils.

While this is not to be regarded as proven, yet for the first time it is apparent that investigation is proceeding along fruitful lines, and vast increases in the understanding of known facets of human diversity can be foreseen in the near future. For instance, despite the association of various manifestations of the Rh blood group system with problems of pregnancy, the reasons for the existence of differences in the system in the first place remain entirely unknown. Likewise no sense has yet been made out of the distributions within the NMS system and many others. One thing seems certain: as with the understanding of variations in human morphology, the solution to such problems in the distribution of simple genetic traits will only come when the concept of race is abandoned as the starting point for biological analysis.

References

Baker, Paul T. 1958. Racial difference in heat tolerance. *American Journal of Physical Anthropology* 16: 287–306.
Biasutti, Renato. 1959. *LeRazze i Popoli Della Terra*. Third edition revised I: 721. Unione Tipografico—Editrice Torinese.

Boyd, William C., 1950. *Genetics and the Races of Man.* Boston, Little, Brown and Company.

Brace, C. L. 1962. "Cultural Factors in the Evaluation in the Human Dentition." *Culture and the Evolution of Man,* M. F. A. Montagu, ed. New York, Oxford University Press.

———. 1963. Structural reduction in evolution. *The American Naturalist,* 97: 39–49.

———. 1964. The Fate of the "Classic" Neanderthals: A Consideration of Hominid Catastrophism. *Current Anthropology,* 5: 3–38.

Campbell, T. D. 1925. *Dentition and Palate of the Australian Aboriginal,* Ph.D. Thesis, University of Adelaide, The Hassell Press, Adelaide.

Chang, Kwang-chih. 1962. New evidence on fossil man in China. 1962. *Science,* 136: 749–760.

Coon, Carleton S., Garn, S. M. and Birdsell, J. B. 1950. *Races.* Springfield, Thomas.

Crick, F. H. C. 1958. On protein synthesis. *Symposia of the Society for Experimental Biology* XII: 138–163.

Davies, A. 1932. A Re-survey of the morphology of the nose in relation to climate. *Journal of the Royal Anthropological Institute* 62: 337–359.

Flannery, Kent V. 1961. Early village farming in southwestern Asia (Mimeographed manuscript).

Garn, Stanley M. and Arthur B. Lewis. 1958. Tooth-size, body-size and "giant" fossil man. *American Anthropologist,* 60: 874–880.

Haag, William G. 1962. The Bering Strait land bridge. *Scientific American* 206: 112–123.

Harris, H. 1959. *Human Biochemical Genetics.* New York, Cambridge University Press.

Hogben, Lancelot. 1931. *Genetic Principles in Medicine and Social Science.* London, Williams and Norgate Ltd.

Hrdlička, Ales. 1920. Shovel shaped teeth. *American Journal Physical Anthropology* 3: 429–465.

———. 1921. Further studies on tooth morphology. *American Journal Physical Anthropology* 4: 141–176.

———. 1924. New data on the teeth of early man. *American Journal Physical Anthropology* 7: 109–132.

Huxley, Julian S. 1941. *Man Stands Alone,* New York, Harper.

Huxley, Julian S. and A. C. Haddon. 1935. *We Europeans: A Survey of 'Racial' Problems.* London, Jonathan Cape.

Keith, Arthur. 1949. *A New Theory of Human Evolution*. New York, Philosophical Library.

Kelso, J. and R. Armelagos. 1962. Nutritional Factors as Possible Selective Agencies in the Determination of A B O Blood Group Frequencies. (Paper read at the annual meeting of The American Anthropological Association, November 18, 1962).

Livingstone, Frank B. 1958. Anthropological implications of sickle cell gene distribution in west Africa. *American Anthropologist* 30: 533–562.

————. 1961. More on middle pleistocene hominids: comments. *Current Anthropology* 2: 117–118.

————. 1962. On the non-existence of human races. *Current Anthropology* 3: 279.

Montagu, M. F. Ashley. 1941. The concept of race in the human species in the light of genetics. *The Journal of Heredity* XXXII: 243–247.

Newman, M. T. 1953, The application of ecological rules to the racial anthropology of the aboriginal new world. *American Anthropologist* 53: 311–327.

Post, Richard H. 1962. Population differences in red and green color vision deficiency. *Eugenics Quarterly* 9: 131–146.

Roberts, D. F. 1953. Body weight, race and climate. *American Journal Physical Anthropology* 11: 533–558.

Thomson, Arthur and L. H. Dudley Buxton. 1923. Man's nasal index in relation to certain climatic conditions. *Journal of the Royal Anthropological Institute of Great Britain and Ireland* 53: 92–122.

Verneau, Le Dr. René. 1906. Anthropologie, *Les Grottes de Grimaldi* (Baoussé Roussé) Tome II, Fascicule I, Imprimerie de Monaco, pp. 1–212.

Weidenreich, F. 1937. The dentition of *sinanthropus pekinensis*: A comparative odontography of the hominids. *Palaeontologia Sinica* 101: 1–180.

Weiner, J. S. 1954. Nose shape and climate. American Journal Physical Anthropology 12: 1–4.

VIII   A Biological View of Race

PAUL R. EHRLICH AND RICHARD W. HOLM

Most of the problems clouding the study and description of human variation can be traced to the taxonomic premise that *Homo sapiens* is divided into a series of races which are significant biological entities. We shall attempt to deal with this premise in the context of current biological thinking about the taxonomic structure of nature.

The historical development of taxonomy follows closely the changing prejudices and philosophies of other sciences and of the humanities and arts as well. At any period taxonomy more or less reflects the prevailing world view of a somewhat earlier historical period. Thus it is understandable that the first formal taxonomy should have been an outgrowth of herbals and bestiaries. The Linnaean system developed in the 18th century along with the pervasive compulsion to order nature into mechanically logical systems. The taxonomic framework of the recent past is the result of the 19th century's propelling need to think in terms of linear progression. Today, however, in many areas of creative activity, there is a growing interest in problems of portrayal, description, and quantification of complex nonlinear relationships. It is not surprising that the impact of these approaches and of the devices necessary to sustain them is now beginning to be felt in taxonomy.

The New Systematics

In recent years, following the lead of the physical sciences and mathematicians, biologists have begun to examine some of and basic tenets and assumptions of their discipline. Taxonomy, often thought of as the least dynamic of the biological sciences, has assumed a position of leadership in this reevaluation of methods and principles. Taxonomy has experienced what might be regarded as two revolutions (see Kuhn, 1962) in the last 25 years. The first led to the establishment of the "new systematics" and derived primarily from the introduction of ideas from genetics and cytology into a largely museum-oriented field. Awareness of the principles of Mendelian genetics and the analysis of large population samples of organisms resulted in a greater interest in infraspecific categories. Thus the concepts of subspecies and geographic races, championed by Rensch, Mayr, Dobzhansky, and others, increased in importance. The commonly acccepted definition of subspecies was well-expressed by Mayr (1942, p. 106):

The subspecies, or geographic race, is a geographically localized subdivision of the species, which differs genetically and taxonomically from other subdivisions of the species.

The new systematics shifted interest away from static species concepts, established by Linnaeus and reinforced, in a sense, by Darwin's emphasis on the term species. Differentiation of populations became the new point of focus and greater understanding was gained of the cytogenetic processes involved. However the problem of the taxonomic expression of the complex interrelationships discovered was largely ignored or attempts were made to solve the problem with the existing taxonomic framework. The new systematics, in introducing dynamics into taxonomy, laid the groundwork for its own replacement. Extensive investigations of organisms in nature and of forms with widely divergent genetic systems (inbreeding, haplodiploidy, asexual reproduction, etc.), together with studies of multivariate patterns of geographic variation, made it apparent that the classical species-subspecies taxonomic structure (partially retained by the "new systematics") was inadequate for the expression of evolutionary relationships.

Perhaps the first signs of aging of the new systematics came in the early 1950's with the wide realization that the entities placed in the category "subspecies" were not necessarily evolutionary units. The subjective nature of the category had long been recognized (Mayr 1942). The dangers of its use were made clear by the controversy following a paper by Wilson and Brown (1953), who pointed out the arbitrary nature of the category and recommended that it no longer be used.

These problems were not unique to the subspecies category. Intensive studies of species, particularly in plants, have shown that the species itself is not necessarily a self-contained evolutionary unit (Epling and Catlin 1950). Attempts to create a rigorous and objective definition of species based on genetic criteria have failed because it is not possible to make them operational. A return to the original definition of species as "kind" has been recommended (Ehrlich and Holm 1962).

The major triumph of the "new systematics" was to introduce evolutionary thinking into taxonomy, and this led to the inevitable failure of the new systematics at the descriptive level. The inclusion of evolutionary hypotheses and assumptions into the word-symbols of taxonomy greatly reduces their usefulness for objective descriptions of patterns of relationships among organisms. If the process of evolution is to be inferred from the classifications of taxonomists, then the classifications cannot be based upon evolutionary hypotheses.

Numerical Taxonomy

The second post-Linnaean revolution in taxonomy began in the late 1950's and its effects are just beginning to be felt by the practicing taxonomist. The proximal cause of this revolution was the growing access to high-speed data-processing equipment. Although for many years taxonomists had recognized the usefulness of taxonomic systems based on multiple character comparisons (see, for instance, Anderson 1949), systems using large numbers of characters could not easily be analysed without the aid of digital computers. As availability of such equipment increased, people in many parts of the world began investigating phenetic relationships (relationships defined as degree of over-all similarity) among organisms. Developments in this field are largely outside the scope of this discussion; they are discussed concisely by Sneath and Sokal (1962) and in detail by Sokal and Sneath (1963). The broader implications of this approach, which perhaps are more concealed than revealed by the commonly used name, numerical taxonomy, are considered by Ehrlich and Holm (1962).

In brief, numerical taxonomy consists of the quantifying of large numbers of characteristics (usually 75 or more) which vary in the group of organisms to be studied. This is followed by the computation of some kind of coefficient of similarity among the units studied, based upon these characteristics. These coefficients may then be used as the basis for a taxonomic system by clustering the most similar entities. A simplified example is given in Figure 1.

The table (upper left) lists three entities, *A, B, C.* These entities may be individuals, species, genera, or any other units which are to be compared. In this example, only seven characters are evaluated for *A, B,* and *C.* A character, in the idiom

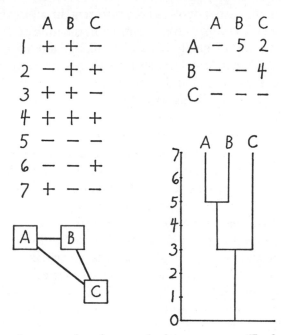

Figure 1. An example of numerical taxonomy. (Explanation in text.)

of the numerical taxonomist, is any characteristic which varies in the group under consideration. In our example, characters which have been coded into two states, plus or minus, have been listed. Certain characters in human beings, such as Rh positive or Rh negative blood types, could easily be coded in this fashion. Coding a character such as height in this manner results in considerable loss of information.

In order to obtain a measure of the degree of resemblance among *A*, *B*, and *C*, a very simple coefficient of association is obtained by counting the number of characters which are the same for each pair of entities. This coefficient may take values from a maximum of 7 (two entities the same in all characters) to a minimum of 0 (two entities different in all characters). Values for all combinations are shown in the table in the upper right. This array of coefficients of similarity among entities is known as a Q-matrix. It can be seen that, with respect to the characters measured, A and B are more similar than A and C, C is more similar to B than to A, and B is more similar to A than to C.

Since only three entities are being compared here, it is possible to diagram these relationships in two dimensions as has been done in the lower left. The higher the coefficient of similarity, the shorter the line connecting any two entities. However, Q-matrices containing coefficients among more than three entities cannot be diagrammed in two dimensions. Nor is it easy by inspection to visualize the multi-dimensional relationships inherent in larger matrices. A matrix showing all of the possible comparisons among, say, 100 species of a genus would contain 4,950 different coefficients regardless of the number of characters employed in the comparisons. In order to obtain some grasp of the relationships in such an array, various methods of searching for and diagramming structure in the matrix have been devised.

The dendrogram (lower right) illustrates one method of structuring applied to our small sample matrix. The ordinate is the scale of values of the similarity coefficient. Since each entity has complete similarity with itself, each is placed at the top of the diagram with a value of 7. The highest coefficient in the Q-matrix is 5, between A and B, therefore the lines are joined at that level. The A-B stem is joined to the C stem at the average value of the coefficients of C with A and C with B (3). The diagram gives a more readily grasped picture of relationships, but only at the cost of the loss of some information present in the Q-matrix. For instance, from looking at the diagram one could not know that C is not equally similar to A and B.

The "taxonomy" of these entities could be viewed as one

taxon comprising two entities (or subordinate taxa) and another taxon comprising one. Various methods of applying nomenclature to dendrograms have been employed but their details need not concern us. The decision of how distinctive a group of entities must be before it should be distinguished (with a number or a name) as a "kind" or "species" is a decision which can only be made in the context of a particular investigation. It is important to realize that clusters derived by such analysis are based solely upon resemblances in the characteristics evaluated and are not based upon genetic or phylogenetic hypotheses. They comprise, however, the basic data set upon which such hypotheses may be constructed.

As might have been expected, such procedures have been decried by many taxonomists as being anti-evolutionary or typological. The first criticism is clearly not valid since the system is not concerned with the possible interpretations of the computed similarities. The second is partially true, although, as several authors (Daly 1961, Sokal 1962) have pointed out, there are fewer objectionable typological aspects to numerical taxonomy than there are to so-called phylogenetic taxonomy. A certain amount of the opposition to numerical taxonomy seems to be based on emotional reactions to the growing use of computers. There are dangers from the misuse of computers as with any mechanism extending human capabilities. Such misuse, if it occurs, is the result of a human decision. Emotional reactions to numerical taxonomy can be found even in the anthropological literature. For example (Coon 1962, p. 13):

The determination of species cannot be made by feeding figures into a computer. It is in a sense an art, practiced by men of experience who know, first of all, how species are formed.

It is true that the so-called art or intuition of practicing taxonomists has resulted in classifications of practical and scientific use. These intuitive classifications, however, also have led to some unfortunate misconceptions as will be discussed below. The rigorous and highly specified procedures of numerical taxonomy largely avoid such problems by limiting greatly the opportunity for personal bias to enter undetected at the stage of gathering data and making comparisons. Coon's statement also illustrates the confusion of data with hypotheses mentioned above.

In some instances, the results of numerical taxonomy have been remarkably congruent with those produced by classical taxonomy. The numerical study retains the advantage, however, of having been done in clearly specified and repeatable steps. The classical taxonomist must depend for the evaluation of a taxonomic work largely upon his personal opinion of its author. Numerical taxonomists may check each other's work by repeating any or all steps. Other advantages of numerical taxonomy, such as precision in estimating relationships and ability to specify questions of character sampling and interrelationships of characters, cannot be discussed here. Most importantly perhaps, numerical taxonomy has retrieved the problem of what is meant by biological relationship from the cloudy realm of art and intuition.

It has long been assumed that satisfactory general classifications of organisms could be based on virtually any sample of the characteristics of individuals. In the past, the majority of these samples consisted of a small number of external characteristics of adult organisms. A few taxonomists have been concerned about the validity of this assumption in holometabolous insects and in plants with alternation of generations. This concern is understandable since larvae and adults or gametophytes and sporophytes may live in quite different environments and may seem strikingly different. Recently, numerical taxonomists have begun to investigate this question. Preliminary results indicate that congruence of taxonomies based on different stages in the life history may not be the rule. For instance, Rohlf (1963) compared the classifications of larval and adult mosquitos using numerical taxonomic techniques. He found significant (but not large) correlations between larval and adult relationships. The sets of relationships were, however, not congruent. He concluded (p. 116):

. . . while there is general agreement between the larval and adult interrelationships, there are also many distinct differences between the classifications. It was recommended that characters should be taken from all life-history stages, if possible, in order to form the most general classification.

Similar difficulties may be found when characteristics of different sexes or different parts of the adult are used in establishing phenetic relationships. Michener and Sokal (1963), for example, have found incomplete congruence in comparing the patterns based on males and females and on head and body characteristics of bees. The taxonomist assumes that the phenotypes he studies are representative of genotypes. The fact that more than one representation of the same genotype may be constructed by studying different stages in the life cycle or different sets of characters from the same stage clearly shows how biased our picture of the genotype may be and how poor is our understanding of the genotype-phenotype relationship.

The magnitude of this problem cannot be judged from the data in hand because so few detailed studies have been made. The data which are available give us little reason to feel sanguine about the precision of inferences about relationships estimated on the basis of small samples of characteristics. When it is remembered that paleontology deals with small samples of characteristics of small samples of organisms, the importance of this problem is easily seen. Little credence can be put in attempts to reconstruct phylogenies at the infraspecific level from paleontological data (as has been attempted by Coon, 1962, in the case of human races). Indeed, the arbitrary subspecific units recognized by Coon almost certainly have no phylogeny to reconstruct. It is difficult enough to trace even major lineages when relatively abundant material is available, as for instance, in the history of horses summarized by Simpson (1951).

A general problem in biology is how to deal with continuous but ever changing phenomena. This problem is especially important for the taxonomist because one of the more unfortunate aspects of the hierarchy inherited from Linnaeus is its requirement for discrete taxa. Therefore continua in space and time must be fragmented by the taxonomist. The patterns created by hybridization, reticulate evolution, apomixis, etc., cannot be adequately expressed by the classical taxonomic structure. Quantified similarities in a Q-matrix are free of this problem, although any *classification* based upon a Q-matrix will inevitably lose some information (but in a predetermined pattern dependent upon the clustering procedure used). Very recently C. D. Michener (1963) has begun to explore ways of making taxonomic classifications more realistic biologically by allowing overlapping taxa. The phylogenetic taxonomist often feels, and always hopes, that his groups represent "real" entities. The numerical taxonomist is always aware of the real source of his groups.

The Subspecies Problem

When one looks at the systems of classification which have been employed by anthropologists, he cannot help but be struck by the diversity of these systems and their tendency to overemphasize differences. Nowhere is this more apparent than in the classification of human subspecies or "races."

The ancient observation that men from different areas may differ in superficial characteristics unfortunately has led to the assumption that man could be divided into some number of biological entities known as races. Beginning as a simple folk taxonomy, the idea of distinct or largely distinct races appears throughout the literature of anthropology. As anthropologists became aware of the new systematics, they naturally attempted to interpret their classifications in the genetic and phylogenetic terms appropriate to this approach.

The genetic definition of taxa seemed particularly suitable since modern *Homo sapiens* is perhaps the only widespread species which has been demonstrated to fit the "biological" species definition. In all probability every significant test of interbreeding within the species has been made under natural conditions and there is no known instance of successful interbreeding with a sympatric species. Indeed, the cytogenetic systems and behavioral mechanisms of the hominoids would seem to preclude the latter. Thus it is convenient to describe man in aggregate as the species *Homo sapiens*. Species is here used to connote *kind* and not to imply some sort of biological equivalence with other species of plants, animals, or microorganisms. We can be certain that *Homo sapiens* is quite a different sort of entity from the coast redwood, the common fruit fly, or *Paramecium aurelia*.

While *Homo sapiens* may qualify (perhaps uniquely) as a biological species, treatment of infraspecific variation in man under the rules of the "new systematics" has not proved so simple. As mentioned above, the arbitrary nature of the subspecies has long been recognized. Two general problems have plagued those who wish to circumscribe infraspecific units in plants and animals. The first is the selection of the characters on whose variation the units will be defined. The second is the decision as to the amount of difference which will be recognized as amounting to subspecific differentiation. This de-

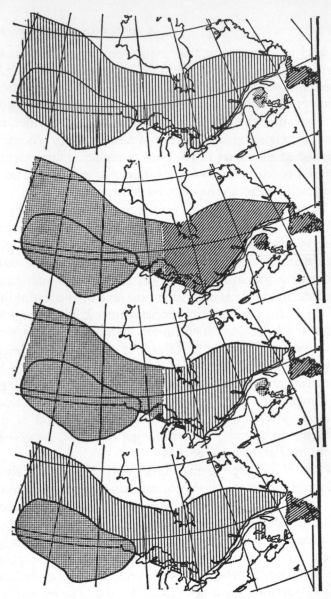

Figure 2. Geographic variation of seven different characters in the butterfly *Coenonympha inornata*. Junctions between different kinds of shading indicate that adjacent populations are significantly different from one another in the particular character

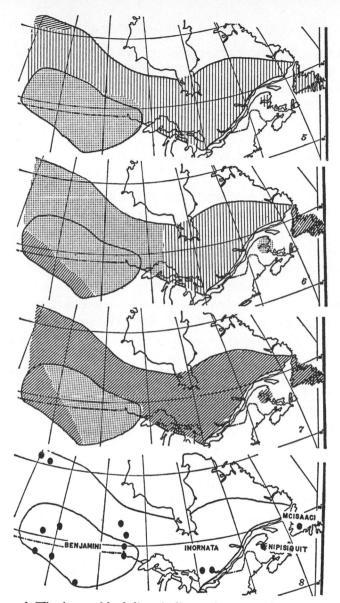

mapped. The heavy black lines indicate the approximate ranges of two of the currently recognized continental subspecies, *inornata* and *benjamini*. *Mcisaaci* and *nipisiquit* are disjunct "subspecies." (After Gillham.)

cision is a matter of taxonomic judgment and the discussion over percent rules and other guidelines for making decisions need not concern us here.

Concordance and Discordance

The question of character selection is of greater moment. If characters are largely concordant (that is, if they tend to vary together), then the study of the variation in any one character, or a few characters, would reveal the patterns in which population differentiation has occurred. If, on the other hand, variation is mostly discordant (characters are largely independent), then population differentiation must be studied with respect to one variable at a time. With discordance predominating subspecies recognized on the basis of one or a few convenient characters would not be evolutionary units. They would be simply units of convenience for filing specimens. Our zeal for discovering evolutionary units is predicated upon the belief, of course, that such units will have greater information content and hence greater predictive value than units recognized on other bases. Units of convenience for filing would not necessarily have these attributes and are not commonly thought of as useful in this way.

Too few studies have been made to permit a clear statement as to whether concordance or discordance in variation prevails in plants and animals. Subspecies in plants often seem to show concordant variation. In those zoological situations which have been analyzed, however, discordance seems to be the rule. For example, Gillham (1956) has analyzed a series of studies of geographic variation in butterflies in which both continental and insular subspecies have been recognized.

His survey revealed widespread discordance, as exemplified by Figure 2. As Gillham puts it (p. 120):

In view of the prevailing discordance of geographical patterns followed by different variates, racial partition of butterfly species is not only arbitrary, but it must also necessarily weight some variates and ignore others, without regard for the biological significance of any of them. The best that can be hoped for now is an analysis of variation by individual characters, avoiding arbitrary subdivision of the species. Such analysis will eventually yield a less distorted picture of species formation than that to which the artificial subspecies now inevitably leads.

It seems fair to state that, as a tool for understanding biological processes, the subspecies has deservedly lost favor. In the past ten years, only a very few papers in the journal *Evolution* have dealt primarily with the subspecies concept.

The Situation in Homo Sapiens

Is man an exception to this trend of discordance in animals? The problem of taxonomic structure within the species *Homo sapiens* is very complex. Certain statements, however, seem almost beyond dispute:

1. There is geographic variation in numerous human phenotypic traits.

2. This geographic variation has a largely genetic basis.

3. Variation in many instances cuts across cultural lines. Furthermore, there is reason to believe that differences among populations are largely the result of the action of selective agents. An inspection of a series of maps of the geographic distribution of human traits shows that the observed variation

patterns are quite discordant. The problem is not solved even if recent migrations are discounted and only so-called aboriginal populations considered. It is obvious that the choice of a characteristic for the primary division will determine in large measure what races will be recognized. The vast majority of classifications which have been proposed thus far, both folk and scientific, have been based primarily on skin color. Had blood groups, hair type, or body build been the primary standard, the lines would certainly have been drawn differently.

Doubtless there are many internal structural and physiological characteristics which are not immediately obvious, but which show geographic variation. Only a few of these have been studied, especially those relating to metabolism and temperature tolerance. As W. L. Brown has aptly put it (p. 152):

Applied to the wealth of data on the variation of modern *Homo sapiens*, the "no race" idea seems worth considering on this basis [discordance of characters], even though the value of the race concept in studies of man has already been challenged widely on other grounds by anthropologists themselves. In the face of such obvious discordance as, for instance, human skin pigmentation with blood type factors, or hair form with cephalic index (taken on a world basis), the wildly varying opinions of anthropological schools on the racial classification of our species show up as irrelevant and unnecessary.

Psychological characteristics, such as intelligence, drive, and disposition, certainly have a genetic basis (Erlenmeyer-Kimling and Jarvik, 1963). Although there can be no doubt that these psychological attributes are in part determined by the genetic information, the problem of estimating the genetic component of the variation in ability to reason abstractly, for example, is difficult in the extreme. In other words, the hereditary endowment of an individual and his environment interact to produce the psychological phenotype. It is virtually impossible to separate the two components completely. While most mental characteristics are highly subject to environmental (particularly cultural) modification, it is clear that the range of possible responses is genetically set. One would expect, therefore, the frequency of the genes concerned to vary geographically. Psychological characteristics undoubtedly show basically the same sort of geographical variation as physical characteristics, even though their environmental component may, in many cases, be greater.

It seems very unlikely that satisfactory tests will be devised in the near future which will permit accurate evaluation of the genetic range of psychological characteristics, even within rather close-knit cultural groups, let alone among diverse cultures. One might expect variation in the genetic range of abstract reasoning ability from culture to culture, perhaps based on weak selection for or against individuals showing a high capacity for abstraction. One might hypothesize that, say, a Chinese population would have a slightly higher or lower average genetic ability for abstraction than one from the United States. It is difficult, however, to conceive of any practical way of testing this hypothesis in the face of overriding cultural influences.

It is generally accepted that attributes like intelligence are composite in nature. There would seem to be a priori no reason to expect concordant variation in the frequencies of genes controlling these various components (if they could be estimated), any more than in those controlling so-called physical characters. It also seems quite clear that geographic variation in genetic components of intellectual traits must be relatively insignificant in comparison with the variation induced by social and cultural environments.

This does not mean that the differences observed among men are some sort of mirage. Eskimos and Ubangis are obviously different in many respects. The crucial question is

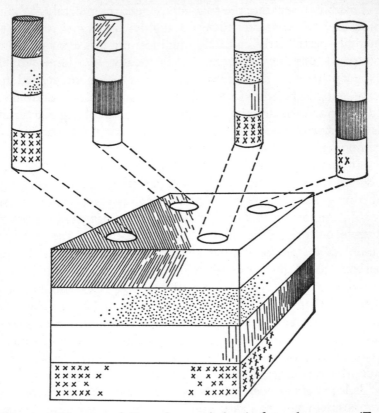

Figure 3. Diagram of discordant variation in four characters. (Explanation in text.)

whether or not one can classify human populations into discrete biological units (races or subspecies) one of which contains, say, the Eskimos and the other the Ubangis. This point is clarified in Figure 3. Each layer in the cube represents the geographic variation in a single hypothetical character. For example, if the top layer represented skin color, individuals in the near left-hand corner would have the darkest skin, those in the righthand half of the cube would have light skin, and so forth. The cores extracted from the cube each represent a sample of individuals taken in that geographic area. Each sample is different; indeed, one might say that each represents a different "race." However, a set of four samples taken at any four places in the "character cube" would also produce four different "races." There is no "natural" racial division because the abundant geographic variation is in discordant characters.

The goal of any system of classification is, or should be, to abstract patterns of variation in such ways that they may be comprehended. Hiernaux (1963) has clearly expressed the crux of the matter (p. 199):

Classification is not a goal in itself, but a tool, a very useful one indeed when it works. When it does not, discarding it will not withdraw any scrap of knowledge, but on the contrary force us to face the facts as they are, in their full complexity.

Present-day subspecific classifications of man do not satisfactorily abstract the patterns of infraspecific variation apparent in *Homo sapiens.* Numerical taxonomic techniques will permit the evaluation of phenetic relationships among different geographic samples of men. It seems unlikely, however, that such analysis would result in sets of relationships which could reasonably be structured into discrete subspecific entities. It would be interesting to determine if discrete clusters exist at any level and if any indication of hierarchical structure exists.

Thing-Concept Confusion

Why then, in the face of these difficulties, do many biologists still feel that "good species" and "good subspecies" must exist in nature and, that, given the time and tools, such entities will be discovered or delimited? The answer may be found in what might be called the "thing-concept confusion." The average biologist, when he says bird, flower, or Negro, feels that he is referring to a real, clearly delimited, biological entity. Although certain items may be referred unambiguously to one or another of these concepts, even a cursory consideration of them reveals that their unity resides primarily in the mind. How are the penguin, the ostrich, and the sparrow related? The systematist would say that they belong to a unit, birds, because of recency of descent from a common ancestor. Unfortunately this answer ignores the question of when, in time, birdlike reptiles became reptilelike birds. The limits of the entity bird become indefinite when the paleontological dimension is considered. The question of how to determine recency of descent is also ignored. One might assert that a penguin's most important biological relationships are with other organisms in their ecological situation such as killer whales, seals, and Antarctic fishes. These relationships at least have the advantage of being amenable to a certain degree of definition. It is only by making value judgments that one can decide which of these sorts of relationship are more important. Many biologists feel that phylogenetic relationship is more important because they can conceive of the transfer of genetic information along lineages back through time. We would not care to make this judgment. The transfer of energy in ecosystems seems equally (or more) significant than transfer of genetic information. In addition little is known about the structure and evolution of ecosystems and the possibilities of exchange of genetic information across what are considered to be phylogenetic lines.

The word flower might be considered to refer unambiguously to a morphological unit. In some plants, however, it is difficult to delimit one flower from another because they are reduced and crowded together in the inflorescence. From the point of view of function, the situation is even more complex.

The familiar poinsettia is an example of a group of very specialized flowers arranged in an inflorescence with brightly colored leaves or bracts. Just as most of us think of a daisy as a single flower although it is a cluster of small florets, so could we regard an entire flowering branch of poinsettia as the ecological equivalent of a flower. Nearly all of the grasslike sedges are wind-pollinated and have inconspicuous flowers. The highly modified, small, and clustered flowers of the sedge, *Dichromena,* however, are surrounded by colored leaves and the whole complex resembles a single flower. This genus of sedge is insect-pollinated. As soon as one attempts to make an exclusive definition, he immediately perceives borderline situations which do not clearly fit within the limits he wishes to impose.

The concept Negro has much in common with the concepts bird and flower. Sociologically, Negro is defined differently in the United States and Brazil. In the southern United States anyone who is not "pure white" is a Negro. In Brazil, anyone who is not "pure black" is a caucasian. Biologically the concept Negro has even less unity. Heavy skin pigmentation may be associated with a wide variety of other characteristics.

It is all too easy to decide from one's mental patterns and prejudices or one's distorted percepts from nature that there is an actual structure out there waiting to be found. This is the phenomenon of reification of concepts, well-known to the historian of scientific thought. This concept-thing confusion may seem unimportant when dealing with, say, subspecies of butterflies. With *Homo sapiens* such confusion creates not only social problems in the present, but perhaps evolutionary problems in the future. The evolution of man is an interaction between classical "biological" evolution and psychosocial or cultural evolution (Ehrlich and Holm 1963, Montagu 1962). In the realm of psychosocial evolution, conflicting ideas may be analogous to alleles at a genetic locus, their relative frequency fluctuating through chance effects and what might be termed cultural selection. In this context, one might view the waxing and waning of ideas concerning the significance of races and racism as a problem in population phrenetics.

The Consequences of the Classical Approach

It might be profitable to look more closely at the harm that is done by continuing to use the classical species-subspecies categories and the usual hierarchic structure. Intellectual damage is done at virtually every level of investigation in both theory and practice. It is difficult to specify the extent of "damage" when it involves misfiling of specimens of grosbeak study skins as pointed out by West (1962) or the arbitrary pigeonholing of butterfly populations as was done by Ehrlich (1955). It is even more difficult to determine the extent to which our understanding of the process of evolution has been distorted by the imposition of the rigid set of taxonomic categories. In a recent textbook on evolution, one finds the statement: "The very hierarchy of genera, families, orders, and so forth is in itself evidence for the correctness of the theory of evolution, for that is the pattern that evolution should cause to develop." Since evolutionary theory has almost always been dealt with in terms of this hierarchical structure it is hardly surprising that our present theory may be misconstrued as automatically leading to such a structure. The systems of relationship established by unbiased procedures lend little comfort to the view that the structure of nature is inherently hierarchic.

There is no question, however, about the harm which has resulted from the extension of this taxonomic approach to considerations of the nature of geographic variation in *Homo sapiens*. It has, among other things, led to the mistaken assumption that arbitrary racial subdivisions of *Homo sapiens* can be considered as evolutionary units in space and time. As has been discussed above, there is no basis for assuming, without extensive genetic study, that any population or any taxonomic group is an evolutionary unit. Discussions of the biological origins and characteristics of subjectively determined races (e.g., Coon, 1963), based exclusively, as they must be, on evolutionary misconceptions, are useful only for strengthening culturally determined prejudices against groups which have reality only in a social, rather than a biological, sense.

One unfortunate aspect of persisting in considering races to be discrete biological entities is seen in discussions of the consequences of interbreeding between supposed races of *Homo sapiens*. Many of these discussions do not accurately represent what is known about the genetics of interfertile ("infraspecific") populations in other organisms. For example, much attention has been drawn to the problem of the supposedly deleterious effects of "racial intermixture." Zoologists and some botanists, by their use of a "biological" species concept, are constrained to regard exchange of genetic material between what they call species as somehow detrimental to the continued existence of the species. Such interchange in effect becomes an illicit process and the biologist may unconsciously regard it as "unnatural." In the minds of some, hybridization comes to be thought of as a process deleterious to further evolutionary differentiation and not as a part of the evolutionary repertoire of the populations involved.

Biologists do not take this point of view about genetic interchange among populations of the same species. Indeed, the presumed existence of such interchange of genes is critical to the so-called biological species concept. Anthropologists and others have sometimes proposed that the supposedly harmful effects of gene exchange at the species level in other organisms occur at the racial level in man. The term hybridization with its psychologically based overtones, or the ugly word miscegenation, are then used to describe what is presumed to be happening.

There is evidence that some infraspecific crosses made in the laboratory between geographically distant populations produce offspring which are relatively inviable. This has been found in butterflies, moths, frogs, and some plants. Such evidence seems largely lacking for crosses within *Homo sapiens*, although it is possible to construct models involving such phenomena as Rh incompatibility in which crossing might prove deleterious to a population. However, there is also some reason to believe that progeny of parents drawn from two different human populations would be, on the average, more fit in the sense of the population geneticist than the offspring of individuals from the same population. There would appear to be no genetic support either for the encouragement or the repression of intergroup gene exchange in man. Indeed, the situation of partially differentiated populations with some gene exchange among them has been postulated to be the ideal state for further evolution.

It is not necessary here to dignify the George Report and similar tracts with a point-for-point refutation. The pertinent facts are well known to biologists and anthropologists and are widely available to the interested layman (Commoner, et al. 1963). It might be maintained by any scientist that it is his duty to publish facts in his discipline as he sees them. This presumably would include speculations based on these facts. While this is clearly so for the more abstruse ideas of basic science, it does not seem reasonable to absolve the scientist of all social responsibility for his views. The question would rarely arise in the domain of pure science, but it arises frequently wherever *Homo sapiens* is concerned. The situation with race finds an interesting parallel in the discussions of the responsibility of nuclear physicists in designing and building nuclear weapons. Surely no one would wish to prescribe rules of conduct in such matters; one must depend upon the judgment and good faith of the scientist.

It seems little enough to ask, however, that the scientist working in areas where any results are of great social consequence should follow the behavioral pattern of scientists in general. His results should first be published in the scholarly literature. Potential social effects of the results should be considered thoroughly. This would be true whether the scientific results concern nuclear fission, cancer-related viruses, extrasensory perception, organic poisons of potential use as pesticides, or the evolution of *Homo sapiens*. Should the work be misinterpreted or be used to further causes which it does not support, it surely is the responsibility of the scientist immediately to make clear the misinterpretation and to disavow the misuse of his work. In the absence of such a disavowal, it may properly be assumed that the scientist supports such use of his work. Definition of the areas of a scientist's responsibility is an important and vexing question and deserves further discussion. It seems obvious, however, that certain types of behavior are to be avoided. A scientific idea of merit does not become part of the formal structure of science by its acceptance by the public at large. Rather, it must be weighed and reworked by the scientific community. It must not become the basis for social actions until it has passed this important test.

In conclusion it may be said that so-called subspecies or races in man, as in many other organisms, are not evolutionary units. They are arbitrarily created to describe certain variation patterns in one or a few characteristics. They have no common genetic pattern nor may their genetic future be predicted. It is an error to believe that human subspecies or races are *things* that may be discussed and compared or whose separate evolutionary development may be traced. Whereas in other organisms use of the subspecies concept may do only intellectual damage by creating a distorted view of nature, in *Homo sapiens* the results are very different. Promulgation of views of races and their supposed properties may have serious and far-reaching consequences both for man's present behavior and for his future psychosocial evolution. In 1768 the botanist von Haller said:

Natura in reticulum sua genera connexit, non in catenam: homines non possint nisi catenam sequi, cum non plura simul sermone exponere.[1]

His words have even greater cogency today when we know so much more about man's evolutionary background, his behavior and culture, and at least some of the possible consequences of his activities.

References

Anderson, E. 1949. *Introgressive Hybridization.* New York, John Wiley & Sons.

Brown, W. L., Jr. 1958. Some zoological concepts applied to problems in the evolution of the hominid lineage. *American Scientist* 46: 151–158.

Commoner, B., *et al.* 1963. Science and the race problem. *Science* 142: 558–561.

Coon, C. S. 1962. *The Origin of Races.* New York, Knopf.

Daly, H. V. 1961. Phenetic classification and typology. *Systematic Zoology* 10:176–179.

Ehrlich, P. R. 1955. The distribution and subspeciation of *Erebia epipsodea* Butler (Lepidoptera: Satyridae). *University Kansas Science Bulletin.*

1. Nature has linked her kinds into a net, not into a chain; men are incapable of following anything but a chain since they cannot express in words more than one thing at a time. *Historia stirpium indigenarum Helvetiae.*

Ehrlich, P. R. and R. W. Holm. 1962. Patterns and populations. *Science* 137:652–657.

———. 1963. *The Process of Evolution*. New York, McGraw-Hill.

Epling, C. and W. Catlin. 1950. The relation of taxonomic method to an explanation of organic evolution. *Heredity* 4:313–325.

Erlenmeyer-Kimling, L. and L. F. Jarvik. 1963. Genetics and intelligence: a review. *Science* 142:1477–1479.

Gillham, N. W. 1956. Geographic variation and the subspecies concept in butterflies. *Systematic Zoology* 5:110–120.

Hiernaux, J. 1963. Discussion of *Geographic and microgeographic races* by M. T. Newman. *Current Anthropology* 4:198–199.

Kuhn, T. S. 1962. The structure of scientific revolutions. *Foundations of the Unity of Science* 2:1–172.

Mayr, E. 1942. *Systematics and the Origin of Species*. New York, Columbia University Press.

Michener, C. D. 1963. Some future developments in taxonomy. *Systematic Zoology* 12:151–172.

Michener, C. D. and R. R. Sokal. 1963. Two tests of the hypothesis of nonspecificity in the *Hoplitis* complex. In preparation. (Cited in Sokal and Sneath, 1963.)

Montagu, A. [*ed.*] 1962. *Culture and the Evolution of Man*. New York, Oxford University Press.

Rohlf, F. J. 1963. Congruence of larval and adult classifications in *Aedes* (Diptera: Culicidae). *Systematic Zoology* 12:97–117.

Simpson, G. G. 1951. *Horses*. New York, Oxford University Press.

Sneath, P. H. A. and R. R. Sokal. 1962. Numerical taxonomy. *Nature* 193:855–858.

Sokal, R. R. 1962. Typology and empiricism in taxonomy. *Journal of Theoretical Biology* 3:230–267.

Sokal, R. R. and P. H. A. Sneath. 1963. *Principles of Numerical Taxonomy*. San Francisco, W. H. Freeman & Co.

West, D. A. 1962. Hybridization in grosbeaks (*Pheucticus*) of the Great Plains. *The Auk* 79:399–424.

Wilson, E. O. and W. L. Brown, Jr. 1953. The subspecies concept and its taxonomic application. *Systematic Zoology* 2:97–111.

IX Taxonomy and Variation in Modern Man

NIGEL A. BARNICOT

The "race question," as it is sometimes called, is really compounded of a number of related but separable questions. Some of these are zoological, having to do with the purposes and procedures of animal classification, while others concern our attitudes, as members of society, towards the biological diversity of mankind and lie more in the realm of ethical judgment. No topic in anthropology provokes more passionate controversy. This is partly because scientists have not always been sufficiently careful in defining and using their terms, a fault which, with its resulting confusions, may be magnified in the writings of laymen who may neither know nor care about nice distinctions. More important, however, in kindling bad feeling are the social implications which are thought to follow from various interpretations of the scientific evidence. It is doubtful whether scientific knowledge ever leads to particular ethical conclusions by a train of inescapable logic, but in practice these two spheres of thought and action interact in many ways. Science describes the nature of the world within which moral choice must operate and if the results of our actions are to be predictable and compatible with the ethical principles which motivated those actions we cannot ignore scientific evidence. Scientific investigation has often forced us to revise our moral valuations and modify our actions accordingly. When it was supposed that lunatics were possessed by devils it was appropriate to treat mental disorders as a kind of wickedness, whereas now we regard it as a type of disease and call in the doctor rather than the priest. Our view of crime is changing in the same direction but is not yet as emancipated from older moral attitudes. Since we are all nurtured in society and cannot escape the pervasive influences of local opinion and precept, it is inevitable that our ethical convictions will at times affect our scientific activities especially if we are investigating things which concern society very closely. They may, for example, impel us towards or away from a particular field of research but they may also influence our selection of facts and our choice of interpretations where the evidence is still in an inconclusive state. Seen in the light of the ideal of scientific objectivity these are human shortcomings; we can only hope that by being aware of our prejudices we can minimize biased observation and illogical reasoning.

It seems to the writer that the race question, in any acceptable scientific sense, is essentially a problem of taxonomy. The gist of the matter is whether the pattern of human genetical variation has a form which makes it either feasible or useful to recognize and define certain geographic groups to which the name races, or some other term, can be applied. This, it should be noted, is only a part and perhaps not a very important part, of the whole subject of human variation but it makes for clarity if the problem is at first narrowly defined and distinguished from other related problems.

It is impossible to review in a short article the great mass of data which is the raw material for any study of human variation. All that can be attempted is to point out some of the limitations of these data, to discuss their bearing on the taxonomic problem and to give a few examples which illustrate the nature of human population variation. Still less is it the writer's aim to revise existing schemes of human classification; on the contrary his intention is to emphasize that they are open to various objections and are of questionable use as instruments in modern research.

Although anthropologists are presumably free to adopt whatever taxonomic schemes and nomenclature they may think fit, it would be stupid and in the end detrimental to ignore animal taxonomy as a whole and to pursue the study of human variation without reference to the knowledge and experience gained in classifying other animals. It may therefore be helpful to start with a few remarks about taxonomy in general and later to pay special attention to the meanings of the terms species and subspecies in present day zoology since it is these lower categories which particularly concern us in the study of man. The writer has found the books of Dobzhansky (1951), Mayr (1942), Simpson (1961), and Cain (1954) especially useful on these subjects in addition to many articles by various authors, a few of which will be referred to in the text.

Some Taxonomic Principles

Though order exists in the external world of nature, classifications do not. They are schemata devised by men to assist them in dealing with complex material and are in this sense artificial. Many kinds of scientific work, both pure and applied, would not be possible unless the vast array of organic variation were reduced to some manageable system of named categories for identification, reference, and contemplation. Although, as a student of variation, the taxonomist can hardly fail to be interested in the processes which give rise to biological diversity much of his work is utilitarian and in constructing systems of classification he must often reach a compromise between theoretical ideals and practical needs. In evaluating classifications of man this question of utility is important, as Washburn (1962) has stressed. A formal grouping of mankind into named classes may or may not be a satisfactory way of presenting certain facts of human variation in a concise form but it is seldom useful and never necessary in specifying the nature of the material used in a particular scientific study. This can always be done by giving whatever information, either cultural or biological, may be needed to distinguish a particular population from others, as Penrose (1952) has pointed out. It need hardly be mentioned that the legal definitions in use in some multiracial societies are designed to suit their local political needs and usually have little or nothing to do with biological taxonomy.

Although classifications are artificial they are not necessarily arbitrary. The categories into which the material is divided may correspond to real discontinuities in the array of things classified and the arrangement of categories may reflect relationships which do not merely depend on the rules which we adopt. An indefinite number of different criteria might be used to sort animals into groups on the basis of their resemblances and differences but if the number of criteria is too restricted inconsistencies are likely to arise. A standard example is the class of "animals with wings" which is easily seen to be heterogeneous when other properties are also considered. The taxonomist usually prefers to found his classification on an assessment of overall similarities and differences reached by a study of many attributes. Some authorities refer to such a classification as "natural" but others mean by this a classification which is consistent with our knowledge of evolutionary relationships.

There were, of course, classifications of man and animals before the theory of evolution gained acceptance and they involved metaphysical or theological principles. Today, however, relationship in the evolutionary sense provides a rational basis for taxonomic grouping. Resemblances between animals are often due to common ancestry but they may also arise by independent acquisition of similar features. The taxonomist who accepts phylogeny as a guiding principle must therefore try to distinguish these two situations and shape his classification accordingly. Since, however, the resemblances on which classifications are based are themselves an important part of the evolutionary evidence, circular reasoning is apt to result unless appeal to independent sources of evidence, such as fossil remains, can be made. Doubts about the logical consistency of orthodox taxonomic procedures have recently led some workers to take a more strictly empirical approach founded on quantification of resemblances and analysis of the data by statistical techniques. The case for numerical taxonomy, as it is sometimes called, has been well argued by Sneath (1961) and the opposing point of view has been cogently presented by Simpson (1961). The relevance of Darwin's theory to anthropology was stressed by Huxley (1865) in a famous essay, and Darwin himself dealt at length with the question of human evolution in *The Descent of Man* (1871). It is not always entirely clear, however, to what extent many of the classifications of man published at this period and later were molded by evolutionary ideas. Some authors at least, for example Deniker (1900) recognized the limitations of their system from this point of view, and Haddon (1924) it seems abandoned the attempt to provide more than an orderly list which did not claim to reflect evolutionary relationships.

The Species Concept

The view that there is more than one species of man living today is now rare enough to be regarded as eccentric. Nevertheless it is important to consider the reasons why this view is generally rejected and these can only be understood if the modern concept of a species is first explained. Animal variation, viewed as a whole, is not a continuum but shows definite gaps which enable us to distinguish sharply between animals of different kinds. The species *Homo sapiens*, for example, is composed of individuals who are by no means identical but resemble each other quite closely in many ways and can all be distinguished without doubt from members of, say, the species *Gorilla gorilla*, or indeed from any other creature alive today. As a preliminary definition we might say that species are the elementary units at which we arrive when we sort collections of animals into mutually exclusive groups. To this we may add the important functional criterion that a species also has a reproductive or genetical unity. In the typical case members of a species are interfertile but either do not mate with or do not yield fertile offspring with members of other species *under natural conditions*. In genetical terms the species is a closed breeding unit within which gene flow is possible but which does not exchange genes with other species. This genetical isolation has important evolutionary implications because the gene pool of the species is thereby cut off from other gene pools and may pursue an independent course of evolutionary change. We need not, in fact, insist on complete genetical isolation though this is the requirement for irrevocable evolutionary independence. If gene flow between populations is too slight to counterbalance processes making for divergence genetical differences between them will gradually increase until barriers to gene exchange ultimately become complete. We may expect occasionally to find transitional states in the formation of species and such cases are especially interesting to the student of evolutionary mechanisms though they may be less popular with the so-called museum taxonomist (that abused and perhaps partly mythical figure) who is too busy docketing and pigeonholing to welcome awkward cases.

In practice the taxonomist usually has to work with limited samples of preserved material. His criteria in identifying and establishing species are mainly anatomical and often restricted to certain parts of the body such as the skin or skull. It is important to realize, however, that species may often be as clearly distinguished by behavioural, biochemical, or even pathological characteristics as by anatomical ones. The taxonomist may also have no direct information about the breeding behaviour of the animals he is studying but he may be able to infer that reproductive barriers exist from the absence of intermediate forms in his collections.

We are not faced with these particular difficulties in studying man for we have observations and material from many parts of the world in considerable abundance. This is not to say that the quality of this material could not be improved or that there are no serious gaps in our knowledge, but even so the data are probably more varied and extensive than for any other species.

It is clear enough when we examine maps of the distribution of human physical characters whether they be anthropometric measurements or variations due to single genes (see Figures 1a, 1b, 2a, 2b) that there are seldom sharp boundaries but rather gradients of change which are more or less steep in different places. This was evident to naturalists like Blumenbach and Buffon more than one hundred and fifty years ago, and they already stressed the element of artificiality in dividing mankind into groups. Some writers, like Topinard (1878) argued however, that at least the most contrasted human population should be regarded as species because the differences between them were judged to be as great as those which distinguish various other mammalian species. This view takes into account only part of the evidence and is quite inadequate in terms of the modern species concept.

We need mention only briefly various difficulties which

arise in applying the species concept in animal taxonomy since they are hardly relevant to the anthropology of modern man. If two populations live in different regions so that the possibility of interbreeding is excluded the genetical criterion of species cannot be applied and a judgment must be made by comparing the degree of difference between them with that observed in related sympatric species. There are other awkward cases in which two populations which do not interbreed where they are in contact are nevertheless connected by a sequence of forms between which some gene exchange is possible. Then again there are so-called sibling species which are virtually indistinguishable by morphology but are reproductively isolated in nature. The genetical species concept breaks down in the case of asexually reproducing forms which produce large clones of genetically identical individuals.

There is an inherent difficulty in applying the species concept in palaeontology and this should be stressed because failure to appreciate it can confuse the interpretation of human as well as other fossil evidence. The delimitation of species in a continuous lineage is a different matter from distinguishing them in space at any one time level and must, like any other division of a continuum, be essentially arbitrary. This in itself may not matter provided the criteria for division are clearly laid down and adhered to; but there may be trouble if different workers use different criteria and do not appreciate their arbitrary nature. It is possible that in a very complete fossil sequence marked variations in evolutionary rates at certain periods might interrupt the regular tenor of change and make the delimitation of successive forms in the sequence less arbitrary. In practice gaps in the geological record have this effect and make it possible to distinguish more or less well-demarcated stages to which generic, specific and subspecific names can be attached. The genetical criterion of species which is valuable in dealing with contemporaneous populations cannot be ap-

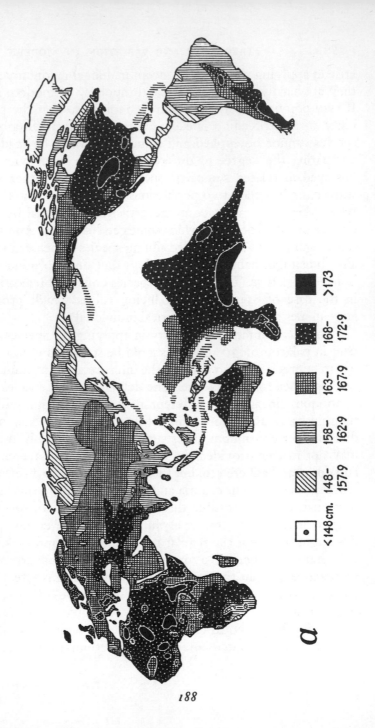

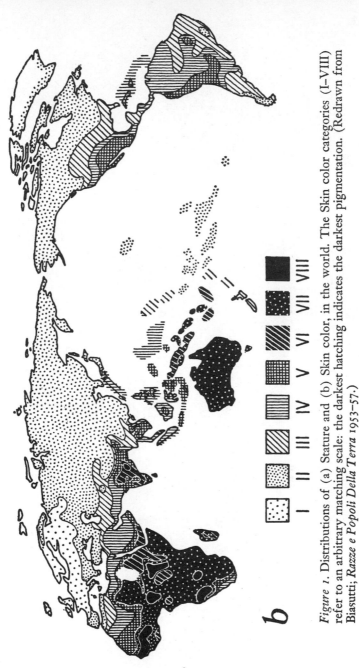

Figure 1. Distributions of (a) Stature and (b) Skin color, in the world. The Skin color categories (I–VIII) refer to an arbitrary matching scale: the darkest hatching indicates the darkest pigmentation. (Redrawn from Biasutti; *Razze e Popoli Della Terra* 1953–57.)

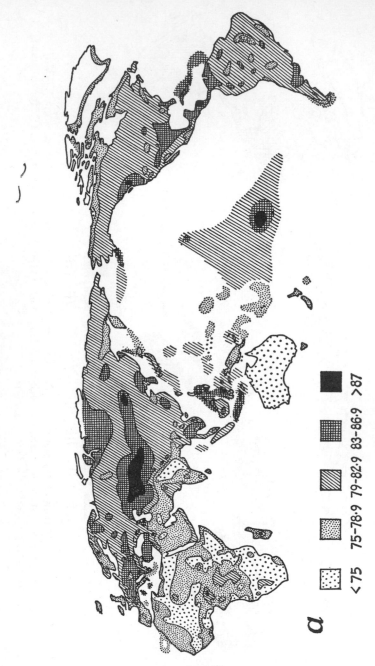

a   <75   75–78·9   79–82·9   83–86·9   >87

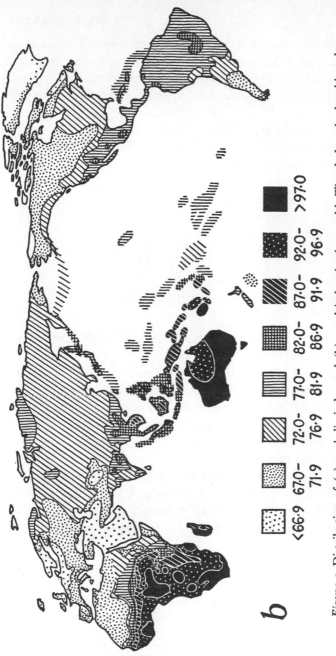

b   <66·9   67·0–   72·0–   77·0–   82·0–   87·0–   92·0–   >97·0
               71·9   76·9   81·9   86·9   91·9   96·9

Figure 2. Distribution of (a) cephalic index and (b) nasal index, in the world. The darker the hatching the broader the head in relation to its length and the wider the nose in relation to its length. (Redrawn from Biasutti; *Razze e Popoli Della Terra* 1953–57.)

plied and makes no sense in the case of an ancestor-descendant sequence. Taxonomic rank appropriate to a given degree of differentiation has to be judged in relation to current practice in classifying contemporaneous representatives of divergent lineages.

Fossil material again, and not least in man, is often fragmentary so that only a limited part of the skeleton may be known and this should compel caution in assessing relationships. The present tendency, it may be noted, is to reduce the taxonomic rank of fossil hominids and to include, for example Pithecanthropus in the genus *Homo*, perhaps as a separate species, *H. erectus*.

Interfertility of Human Populations

In rejecting the idea of multiple human species we do not need to rely simply on the intergrading pattern of human geographical variation which is evident in appropriate maps for we have much direct evidence on interfertility. Since this is an important subject in its own right and one which at times has aroused sharp controversy, it may be useful to say something about it at this point though it is to some extent a digression from our main theme.

It was already recognised long before Darwin's day that good species do not as a rule interbreed, or if they do so in captivity the hybrids are usually sterile, and although in the 18th and earlier part of the 19th centuries the concept of species centered round the question of independent creation, the criterion of intersterility was not ignored. Authorities who believed in multiple human species put forward whatever evidence they could to show that crosses between some of the major geographical variants of man were relatively infertile or that the hybrids suffered from physical handicaps. Much of this evidence, as Darwin and other critical naturalists perceived, was doubtful because it rested on selected cases reported by untrained or even prejudiced observers and because it did not take into account the effects of inferior environment on reproductive performance.

Sterility barriers between animal species may take many forms varying from mating failure, due to uncoordinated courtship behaviour, to defective fertilisation, embryonic development or sexual maturation due to chromosomal and other genetic disturbances. The net result may be failure to produce offspring, a deficiency of offspring as compared with matings within the species, or reduced viability or fertility of the hybrid progeny.

Many human populations are reproductively isolated by distance or by mountains, oceans, deserts and suchlike obstacles, but man is a conspicuously far-ranging species and advances in technology have rapidly reduced the importance of these barriers. There are also cultural barriers, whether of language, religion, class or caste which hinder the random flow of genes and tend to subdivide the species into numerous breeding units. There is no good reason to postulate, however, that there are psychological barriers to interbreeding other than those due to early conditioning to cultural norms. We need only think of the great variety of matings, often on a large scale, that have taken place between Europeans and other peoples to realize that, in suitable circumstances, these barriers are ineffectual.

Human reproductive performance may be affected not only by genetic constitution but by conscious behaviour in relation to social codes and economic needs, by unconscious psychological mechanisms and by acquired disease. To distinguish the genetical component in overall fertility requires careful control of these other variables. It is true that not all possible interpopulation crosses have been observed and some, for example between Eskimos and Bushmen, have probably never occurred. It is also true that the problem of fitness, in the Darwinian sense, in interpopulation crosses would repay more careful study by modern methods; but when this has been said the fact remains that appreciable effects on fitness, due to genetical differentiation between the parental populations, have not been detected.

It is fair to add that plausible arguments can be advanced for expecting some effects. If it is agreed that genetical differences between human populations have mostly been produced by natural selection as adaptive responses to particular environments it is reasonable to ask whether crossing between them may not result in diminished fitness of the hybrid populations. It should be stressed that we are speaking here of statistical effects which might be detectable in large population samples but would not be observed in every individual mating. The problem is very complex and any general answer is sure to involve so many unproven assumptions as to be unrealistic. We can see, however the kind of thing that could occur in the case of certain genes which we have good reasons to think are subject to strong selective forces. The sickle-cell gene, which is virtually lethal in the homozygous state, has nevertheless been maintained at high frequency in some populations because the heterozygotes are less likely to die of malignant tertian malaria in infancy than the normal homozygotes (see Allison 1961). The frequency of the gene is expected to reach a stable equilibrium at a level depending mainly on the local severity of malaria as a selective agent. We may imagine two populations, one of them (A) which has lived for a long time in a highly malarious region and has a sickle-gene frequency adjusted to a high level and another (B) living in a nonmalarious environment and lacking this gene. If population (B) enters the country of population (A) and breeds with it the sickle-gene frequency in the hybrid population will be below that of (A) and this population will experience a greater mortality from malaria than (A) until in time the gene frequency rises to the equilibrium level. On the other hand the parental population (B) in this environment would be subject to an even higher mortality from malaria than the hybrids.

It is clear from such simple and probably oversimplified, examples that in judging the advantage or disadvantage of the hybrid population we must specify which of the parental populations we are comparing it with and in which environment. In addition we are considering the effect on fitness of a single gene in relation to a single selective.agent; it may be that the effects of other genes and other selective agents have a contrary action and that *overall* fitness of the hybrids may be unchanged or even raised. Even more important, the assumption that the relevant environmental factors remain constant is likely to be unrealistic. Population crossing is generally associated, especially today, with considerable change of environment as, for example, when tropical peoples emigrate or are taken to temperate zones or when Europeans entering the tropics bring modern medical techniques with them.

Anyone who is prepared to argue from examples of the kind given above that race-crossing, as it is often called, should be prohibited would do well to consider whether the social conflicts engendered by discrimination may not have detrimental effects far greater than any that are likely to result from biological causes.

Subspecies, Races, and Demes in Zoology

We must now return to the more strictly taxonomic aspect of the race question and discuss differentiation within species rather than between them. With the growth of collections and more detailed examination of good species throughout their whole range of geographical distribution it became clear that many of them were not uniform (monotypic) but showed local differentiation. At the same time it was realised that some forms which had previously been given specific rank were really members of intergrading local populations. This situation was first clearly appreciated in certain groups, such as birds, which had been studied in great detail, but it is not confined to them and in varying degree is probably quite general. The concept of the polytypic species was introduced to accommodate species composed of differentiated subpopulations capable of interbreeding at their zones of contact and therefore incompletely isolated genetically. The name subspecies for such infraspecific groups was officially recognised in 1947 and a third, subspecific name was thus added to the Linnaean binomial, but its use was not made obligatory. The old term variety, which was widely used in approximately this sense in Linnaeus' day and later, is now relegated in zoology to the description of individual variants. The terms geographical race and biological race for local populations within a species distinguished either anatomically or by features of behaviour or physiology, are still sometimes used but lack official status and most taxonomists seem to regard them as synonymous with the term subspecies. The word "race" then, in zoology may be rather vague but it is at least not disreputable. It should perhaps be mentioned here that to speak of "the human race" is a literary rather than a zoological convention.

These changes in taxonomic knowledge led to revision of certain groups and a welcome reduction in the numbers of recognised species; but relief that the rising tide of specific names had been stemmed was temporary for an embarrassing proliferation of subspecific ones soon followed. Burt (1954) for example, noted that there were already 150 named subspecies of the pocket-gopher, *Thomomys bottae*. For this and other reasons, some of which will be mentioned below, the subspecies concept has in turn come in for such criticism, notably by Wilson and Brown (1953). Livingstone (1962) has emphasised the relevance of some of these criticisms to human taxonomy.

Subspecies are usually distinguished by one, or a few differences in external anatomy but sometimes by differences in temperature tolerance and other functional attributes. In mammals and birds, for example, they may differ in the colour of the coat or plumage, in body size or in the relative size of parts such as the tail, feet, or wings. It may be found that two samples representing populations inhabiting different regions of the species range consist of individuals which are all clearly assignable to one or other group; but it is often the case that although they differ in the average value of some measurable character the ranges of variation overlap so that only a certain proportion of the specimens can be classified. It therefore becomes necessary to set up an arbitrary rule defining the degree of differentiation that merits recognition by a subspecific name. Some workers accept two populations as subspecifically distinct if 75 per cent of the specimens can be assigned to one or other of them but others demand more stringent standards such as 84 per cent or even 100 per cent. Naturally it requires a good deal of collecting, measuring, and computing to reach taxonomic conclusions in this way.

In considering merely the statistical differences between samples drawn from various parts of the species range the problem is oversimplified, for although these samples may satisfy our requirements for subspecific distinction it may be that other populations in intervening areas show intermediate characteristics. We are then faced with defining a geographical boundary. If the zone of intergradation is quite narrow, corresponding perhaps to some abrupt change of habitat, no serious trouble arises, but often it is wide and we are confronted with an essentially continuous gradient of change extending over long distances. In this situation any boundary lines that are drawn will be entirely arbitrary and indeed unreal. Such clines, as they are called, are not uncommon and there are many examples in the human species. It has often been assumed that subspecific groupings based on the distribution of one, or at most a few characters, will necessarily be concordant with the distributions of other variable characters. This, it seems, may be so for populations isolated in mountains, islands, caves or other restricted and special habitats, but is not usually the case in wider, more continuous regions. In the latter the distribution areas of various characters may not coincide either in size or shape and their clinal trends may differ in steepness or direction. It appears that natural variation within a species is generally not of a kind that conforms comfortably to the needs of a simple taxonomic method operating by division into sharply divided categories. We may, if we wish, recognize and name subspecific groups based on a few selected characters, in the interests of complete and concise cataloging; but we must recognize the arbitrary element in defining them and we must not suppose that this procedure gives more than an inexact and incomplete picture of natural variation. Animal species when examined in detail consist of numerous local populations even smaller in scale than the wider entities to which subspecific names are sometimes given. It is these so-called demes which seem to approximate most closely to the panmictic units of theoretical population genetics. The distribution of demes may be more or less discontinuous so that although the spread of a gene throughout the species is still possible there are many local barriers hindering its progress. Differentiation between adjacent demes may sometimes be considerable. In the deer-mouse, *Peromyscus*, which has been closely studied over a long period in the United States, populations of *P. leucopus nove-boracensis* inhabiting woods a few miles apart were found to be more different than some populations separated by hundreds of miles (Dice 1940).

Patterns of Human Variation and Problems of Grouping

Linnaeus, who first included man in a classification of animals, recognized only a single species, which in the tenth edition of his *Systema Naturae* (1785) he divided into six varieties, four of which (*europaeus, asiaticus, americanus,* and *afer*) correspond roughly to the inhabitants of the major continents. He gave a terse description of the appearance and also the temperamental characteristics of each. A little later, Blumenbach gave an essentially similar grouping under different names and added another variety, the Malay. As knowledge of the world and its people was gradually extended by exploration, classifications became more elaborate partly because newly discovered peoples had to be fitted into the scheme and partly because investigations became more thorough and included more characters. Deniker's classification (1900) already contained twenty-eight groups and even more elaborate versions have been published since, for example, by Eickstedt (1924) and Biasutti (1953–57).

We need not discuss any of these classifications in detail but we may note that they are all constructed on the same principle and have many features in common. Mankind is first divided into a few broad regional groups on the basis of one or two characters, particularly skin color and hair form, and these groups are then subdivided by bringing in other characters such as stature and head or nose form.

The names given to the ultimate groups in these schemes are often borrowed or adapted from linguistic and other cultural classifications (for example, Arab, Berber, Semite, Turco-Tartar) but some are geographical (for example, Mediterranean, East Baltic, Amazonian). Choice of names is of course arbitrary but there is risk of confusion if the same or very similar names are given to groups established by different criteria. The patterns of distribution of physical characters often do not coincide with those of languages and other cultural attributes although they may do so approximately. Morant (1939) shows how variations in anthropometric characters cut across linguistic and political boundaries in central Europe. On the other hand peoples such as the Bushmen, Lapps, or Polynesians are culturally and relatively distinct groups which are also to some extent physically differentiated from their neighbours. Even when cultural groupings coincide fairly closely with biological ones it may still be confusing to use the same names for each because it may lead us to ignore important differences in the nature of these criteria and the factors which affect their variation. The relationship between the distributions of a given physical character and various cultural attributes should be a matter for investigation in any particular case.

In choosing skin color and other differences which were easy to see early classifiers were merely doing what was most practicable at the time and what in fact is still done in much of animal toxonomy today. Whether in the light of modern knowledge, such characters are the best to choose if we are interested in genetical differentiation of populations is a question that will be taken up in the concluding section. That hair form was so often selected as a criterion for making a primary division of mankind is undoubtedly due to the fact that it seemed to yield a small number of large regional groups. Technically the choice was unfortunate because hair form is notoriously hard to record accurately. An arbitrary division of the range of variation into a few classes such as straight, wavy, and curly, into which all populations are then forced, naturally makes the distribution on a map look simpler than it really is. Apart from this, the selection of a single character as a starting point for subdividing populations may not be easy to justify. If the grouping reached in this way does not correspond with those indicated by a study of other characters we may be able to say no more than that we prefer a character which gives us a few broad groups. From an evolutionary standpoint it may be difficult or impossible to show that such a character gives specially valuable evidence about major lines of descent. We certainly cannot say this for hair form and fossils are unlikely to help us. If blood groups are a valid guide to overall genetical similiarities it seems unlikely that African and so-called Oceanic Negroids are at all closely related and to approximate them taxonomically because of their similar hair form may be fallacious. On the other hand the so-called Mongoloid peoples, who are characterized by straight hair among other things, may well be a more closely interrelated group: but there is much regional variation in other characters which are used in demarcating this group and the problem of defining what we really mean when we use the term Mongoloid is by no means easy.

The problem of grouping populations involves two somewhat different questions which we have already mentioned in discussing the subspecies concept but may now consider a little more closely. Firstly, given data on a number of populations (which may be labeled Australian aborigines, English, Eskimos or something else), how can we best express any divergencies between them? Secondly, given the distribution of one or more characters on the map can we discern regional groups and if so how can we define the boundaries between them? It is obvious that for a metrical, continuously varying character such as stature no natural human population is composed of identical individuals and it cannot be adequately characterized by describing a single member. The stature of a population may be investigated by measuring a representative sample and the results can be conveniently presented as a frequency distribution diagram. Such a diagram is constructed by dividing the range of heights into equal, arbitrary intervals and plotting the frequency or number of persons whose height falls in each interval. Provided the samples consist of one sex only and is reasonably uniform in age and provided the population from which it is drawn is fairly homogeneous and not composed of two or more noninterbreeding groups of different average height, the diagram has a bell-shaped form which resembles that of the Gaussian curve of errors fairly closely. The sample is fully described only by the set of measurements but in order to summarize the information compactly it may be characterized by taking the mean or average value as a measure of central tendency and the standard deviation as a measure of variability. The extent of divergence between two populations may then be expressed as the differences between their means. The observed difference is of course only an estimate obtained from limited samples and it must be tested to see how probable it is that it could be due simply to chance in sampling. As far as measurements of the body taken with calipers and suchlike instruments are concerned substantial differences between the averages of some populations can be demonstrated; but for a given metrical character the range of variation of each population often exceeds the differences between their means so that the distributions overlap. In this case persons whose measurements fall in the region of overlap cannot be classified, at least if this character alone is considered. If skin color is measured as a continuous variate by reflectometric methods it is possible to select populations which show little if any overlap (Figure 3) but others could be

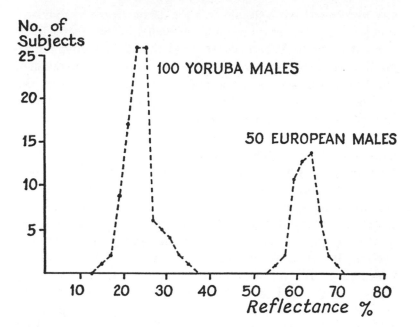

Figure 3. Distributions of reflectance measurements of skin color in a West African (Yoruba) and a European male sample. The reflectance was determined using a red filter and is taken to measure pigmentation due to melanin. (Redrawn from Barnicot, N. A.; Human Biology 30, 150, 1958.)

chosen that would fill the gap between them. Whether two populations are sufficiently distinct to warrant recognition as a subspecies, a race, or some other conventional infraspecific category is an arbitrary matter to be settled by reference to some agreed rule such as the 75 per cent Rule already referred to above.

In anthropometric surveys various measurements of the head, face and other body regions are usually recorded in addition to stature. Each population can then be characterized by a set of average values. The idea of an "average man" con-

structed from such a set of means is deeply rooted in anthropology and is not without value provided his abstract nature,
is not forgotten. When we are told that the Nordic race is
tall, blonde and long-headed this is presumably to be taken as
an abbreviated statement of average tendencies but in this
qualitative form it is so vague that it is apt to be misleading.
We can form an idea of the nature and magnitude of the
anthropometric differences between populations by scanning
lists of average values for various characters. It is useful
however to be able to combine the information provided by
various characters into a single figure which may be used to
measure overall divergence between them. Karl Pearson introduced the Coefficient of Racial Likeness for this purpose but
it was severely criticised and other distance statistics, as they
are usually called, have since been devised. The Generalised
Distance or D^2 statistic of Mahalanobis and the Size and
Shape statistics of Penrose are designed to measure multivariate distances and they have been applied to a number of
anthropological problems. These procedures are a useful refinement of descriptive method but it is important to realise
that it still remains for the biologist to evaluate the implications of the differences so described. Cavalli-Sforza and Edwards (1964) have recently made a preliminary investigation
of a related but more complex problem. They selected 15
populations to represent various major geographical regions
and estimated the degree of divergence between them on the
basis of many anthropometric characters and also the frequencies of a number of blood group genes. They then used
this information to construct a dichotomous tree representing phylogenetic relationships between them. The patterns
of relationship obtained from blood groups on the one hand
and anthropometric data on the other were similar, though
there were a few striking discrepancies, and both were fairly
consistent with orthodox schemes of classifications reached

by less precise methods. The extent to which such a tree provides a reliable picture of actual evolutionary relationships depends on the validity of the various simplifying assumptions that had to be made in constructing it and it is difficult to see how some of them can be checked.

A point to be noticed about all these approaches to the problem of classification and relationship by means of multivariate statistics is that equal weight is given to all characters. This is contrary to the view of most taxonomists who believe that certain characters are more valuable than others as clues to ancestral relationships. Differential rates of evolutionary change in various characters are in fact familiar to paleontologists, and this being so, crucial evolutionary information embodied in a few characters may be swamped if many others are added indiscriminately. Perhaps the main value of a statistical approach to these questions is that the analytical procedures adopted are at least standardized even if they are not free from arbitrariness and that in attempting a precise treatment the logical structure of the problem is more clearly exposed to view.

Some differences between human populations are of a kind which has to be recorded by counting rather than by measurement. In the case of the ABO blood groups for example the vast majority of individuals can be assigned to one of four types, A, B, AB or O and the population can be characterised by giving the frequencies of these types or the frequencies of the genes on which these variations depend.

Many anatomical variations are also essentially discontinuous though in some instances there may be difficulties in defining the boundaries between classes. Skulls can be classified into those which have a persistent metopic suture on the frontal bone and those which do not, or into those which have a so-called Inca bone in the occiput and those which lack it. The palmaris longus muscle of the forearm and its tendon are often greatly reduced and figures for the incidence of this anomaly in various populations are sometimes given; but there are gradations in the extent of reduction of this muscle and it is doubtful whether all individuals can be assigned to one or other class without ambiguity. The same is true when we try to classify hair color as red and non-red for we find that obvious red colors merge insensibly into red-blonde and red-brown colors, and there is little doubt that there are also gradations in eye colours, though it is conventional to divide them into classes such as grey, blue, brown, etc.

Many new blood group systems have been discovered in the fifty years since blood groups were first used to compare populations and many new variants have been described in some of these systems. In addition we now know of numerous inherited qualitative differences in the haemoglobin of the red cells and in various proteins of the serum. The rate of discovery in this field has been so rapid that very few populations have been examined anything like completely and many have hardly been studied at all. Nevertheless we already have a large body of data on the geographical distribution of these serological and biochemical variations and because their inheritance follows Mendelian rules very clearly they constitute our best material for studying population divergence at the genetical level. The characteristics of a population can be represented by a set of frequencies for various genes or the phenotypic classes to which these give rise. In Figure 4 the patterns of gene frequencies with respect to four blood group systems (ABO, MNS, Rh, and Duffy) are shown for five populations.

In the case of discontinuous traits it may happen that all individuals in a particular population are identical in that they all possess or all lack a particular variant, but this is extremely unlikely to be so when other variants are also taken into account. It should also be noted that in the case of discontinuous

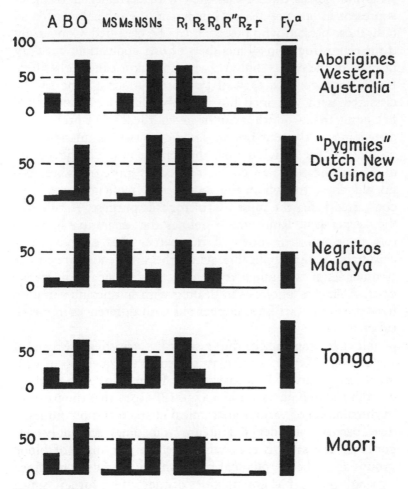

Figure 4. Diagram to show the patterns of gene frequency variations in five populations with respect to four blood group systems ABO, MNS, Rh and Duffy (Fy). The dotted horizontal line indicates a gene frequency of 50 per cent.

traits individuals can be classified with certainty if the trait is present in one population but not in the other but even so only those persons who possess it can be classified. Conversely if the trait is found in all members of one population, but only in some of the others, only those who lack it can be classified. If the trait occurs in each of two populations no one can be classified with certainty but a probability of an individual belonging to one or other can be given, the level of probability depending on the trait frequencies in the two populations and on whether the individual has the trait or not. The likelihood of misclassification is of course reduced if more traits are considered, those for which the population frequencies are most contrasted being the most useful for this purpose. A rule like the 75 per cent Rule which defines the separation between two populations in terms of the percentages of individuals classifiable is not applicable when the differences are in the frequencies of continuous traits, or is only applicable in special cases. Animal taxonomists in dealing with subspecific variation have usually in fact been concerned with differences in metrical characters.

Having emphasized the essentially statistical nature of population differences we may return to the question of geographical variation. It is easy to see from maps such as those reproduced in Figures 1 and 2 (pp. 188–191) that the patterns of distribution of various anatomical characters show no more than partial coincidence and are sometimes strikingly discordant. The same is true when we examine maps of blood groups and other serological or biochemical traits determined by single genes. The complexities of the pattern for any single character and the even greater complexity which results when we superimpose the patterns of a number of them, can only be fully appreciated by studying the maps themselves. If however we select particular populations from various parts of the world these discordances are manifest in the contradictory

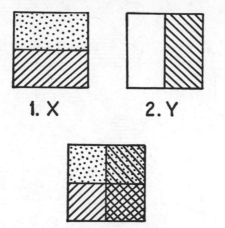

Figure 5. Diagram to illustrate the principle that characterization of populations by multiple attributes, the geographical distribution patterns of which do not coincide, leads to increased complexity of classification (see pp. 209–210).

evidence provided by different characters when we try to assess their resemblances. For instance African and Australian aborigines are both dark-skinned populations but they differ in hair form, and whereas Australian aborigines and American Indians resemble one another in having low frequencies of blood group B the former have low group M frequencies and the latter unusually high ones.

Lack of coincidence between the distribution pattern of various characters inevitably leads to increasing complexity of a classification as more characters are taken into account. To illustrate the point in a very simplified schematic form (Figure 5) the distribution of character X may lead us to define two groups and we may also distinguish two groups when we examine character Y; but if the distribution patterns do not coincide we may find ourselves with four groups when

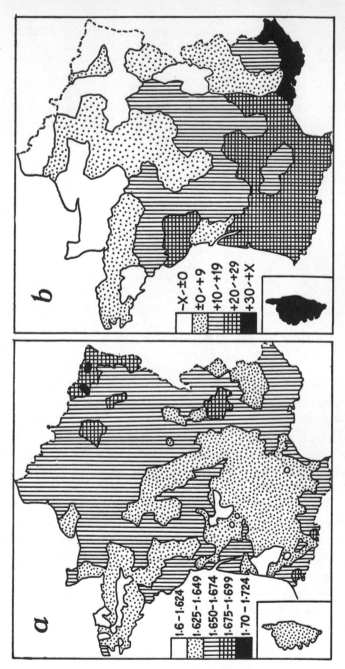

a

	1.6 – 1.624
	1.625 – 1.649
	1.650 – 1.674
	1.675 – 1.699
	1.70 – 1.724

b

	–X ~ ±0
	±0 ~ +9
	+10 ~ +19
	+20 ~ +29
	+30 ~ +X

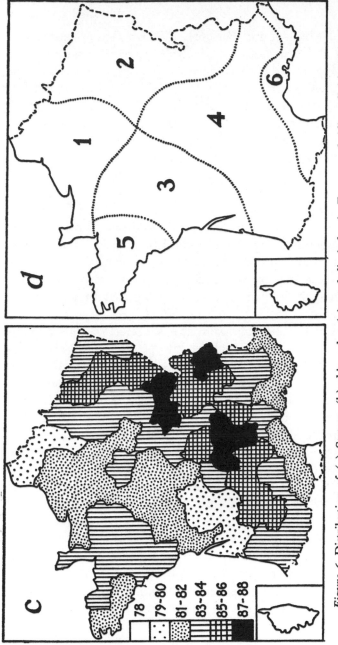

Figure 6. Distribution of (a) Stature (b) skin color (c) cephalic index in France and (d) a division into zones based on the joint information given by these three characters. Darker hatching indicates higher statures, darker skins and relatively broader heads. (Redrawn from Vallois, Anthropologie de la population française 1943.)

we consider both X and Y jointly. Vallois (1943) reproduces maps of the distributions of three physical characters in France (Figure 6). The pattern of geographical variation in each of these is different but by combining the information he then divides the country into six zones, the first containing a tall, blonde mesocephalic population, the second a tall, blonde brachycephalic one, etc. This certainly gives some information about the physical characteristics of the populations in various parts of France but it must be noticed that the distribution pattern of each of the three characters is to some extent graded and shows local irregularities. The dividing lines between the six zones are therefore arbitrary and do not correspond to any sharp natural boundaries. There is no objection to this procedure provided its limitations are remembered and we are not deceived by the sharp boundaries we ourselves have created into believing that they have objective reality.

It may indeed be the case that if we select various populations from a large area such as Europe the multivariate distances between them are less than the multivariate distances which separate them from populations in some other large areas such as tropical Africa or eastern Asia; but it may nevertheless be difficult to define any clear boundaries between the populations of these areas. It seems that certain genes such as V, S^u, Js^a may be largely restricted to Africa, though we do not yet know their distribution in detail, and that African populations also tend to be distinctive in their high frequencies of the Rhesus gene Ro and their very low frequencies of the Duffy gene Fy^a. There are however indications of gradients in the frequencies of these genes in the Horn of Africa and passing into the Near East (see "A survey of some genetical characters in Ethiopian tribes" 1962). Similarly the Diego blood group gene Di^a appears to be restricted to the Americas and Eastern Asia, a zone containing populations which are often distinguished by the term Mongoloid; but within this region its frequency is very variable and it reaches its highest values in South America where the morphological features which are taken to be characteristic of Mongoloids are not pronounced*. We may say as a generalization that the peoples of Polynesia are tall, broad-headed and have high group A, group M and type R_2 frequencies and these characteristics distinguish them from other populations further west; but although there seems to be a relatively narrow zone of division somewhere around Fiji it is still only a zone which is difficult to define precisely not only because single characters show gradations but because the marginal distribution of different characters do not coincide very exactly.

The obvious way to study the distribution pattern of physical characters is to plot population averages or frequencies on a map and we have made use of such maps in this article. It must be realised, however, that this method has pitfalls and practical limitations. Perhaps ideally we should draw a grid on the map and then collect and examine random samples from each grid-square, but in practice we make use of the fact that populations are divided into nations, tribes, and other social units which in general live in a particular geographical area, though it may not always be easy to define this area exactly. This procedure also has some theoretical justification because as geneticists the units which interest us particularly are isolates or Mendelian populations which form, to a greater or lesser extent, closed breeding units; but the

---

* It may be noted here that when we speak of Mongoloids it is not very clear what we are talking about. The tendency is to think in terms of an idealized type with straight hair, yellow skin, epicanthic fold, etc., but this is an abstraction which obscures the fact that in actual Asiatic populations these various characteristics are found in varying degrees in different places. If, as sometimes happens, there is a dispute as to whether a particular skull is Mongoloid this is largely a pseudo-problem generated by our failure to define the term properly.

relation of our sample as defined by a particular name to the breeding structure of the population in the area is a matter which needs to be investigated in any given case. A word like Hausa, for example, applies to a political unity which was welded out of various tribal entities and may well be heterogenous from a biological point of view. In many instances samples are collected in urban centers and we may not know in any detail what area on the map it represents since its members may come from many surrounding places in varying proportion. Other difficulties arise if a population living in a certain area is stratified socially; India is an outstanding example of this and it is known that, at least in some regions, there are fairly well-marked biological distinctions between different levels of the Hindu caste hierarchy. We have, as it were, variation in the social as well as the geographical dimension and any map which ignores this is likely to be misleading. The same applies to social class differences in Europe and elsewhere. Differences of average stature between samples of varying economic level have frequently been demonstrated and in making regional comparisons, we may be misled if the samples representing different areas are drawn from different economic classes. In some parts of the world there is great variation between local populations at least with respect to some characters and if we have data only on a few it may be rash to accept them as representative of a wider area. We find this kind of thing for some blood group genes in New Guinea (see Barnicot 1964) and small tribal groups in India are notoriously variable. Very often in fact our material for a particular region is lamentably thin, not only in the sense that only a few of the component populations have been examined but that our samples of these are small and our averages or frequencies correspondingly inaccurate. When average values or frequencies are entered in the appropriate position on the map we cannot tell without referring to the original data how reliable, in the statistical sense, they may be. If in addition we have very few points to represent a large area it can be very misleading to replace them by contour lines since the course of these must be largely guesswork and the resulting map conceals the paucity of data. Obviously in drawing contour lines the size and position of the grouping intervals which are chosen make some difference to the final pattern but this should not matter much if the material is abundant. One curiously unrealistic feature of many such maps is that contour lines and hatching are continued over areas which are practically uninhabited not to mention areas for which we have no data. Many of the difficulties mentioned above can be overcome by collecting more data and collecting it more carefully, but some of the older maps in the literature, especially of anthropometric characters, may indeed need critical checking.

To summarize what has been said in previous pages, there are differences of a statistical kind between the peoples of different regions but the geographical pattern of variation seems as a rule to be such that regional groups can only be arbitrarily defined and no one in fact has yet suggested precise definitions. Unless we are prepared to specify the magnitude of the differences which qualify a population to be called a race and unless we are prepared to define the geographical boundaries which demarcate one race from another, the term can only have a vague meaning and as such may easily lead to misunderstandings.

One semantic point is perhaps worth noting because it has sometimes led to confusion. If a race, or whatever term we may prefer to use, is defined by certain characteristics, then the word racial should only be applied to those characteristics which contribute to the definition. It may be that races, so defined, will be found to differ in various other physical characters but these may add nothing to the definition and

may indeed contradict it if their distributions do not correspond to those of the defining characters. A related error
it to speak of racial differences when we really mean genetical
differences. While it is true that racial differences should be
genetical, all genetical differences between populations should
not be called racial because they may not all contribute to the
definition of groups.

The Genetical Component in Human Variation

Genetical questions lie at the core of many problems of
biological variation whether in space or in time. We have
inevitably touched on these at several points in the preceding
pages but it remains to develop this important aspect of our
theme more fully. It is a basic assumption implicit in modern
animal taxonomy that the characteristics used for the purposes
of classification shall be inherited in the biological sense. From
an evolutionary point of view continuity within a lineage
depends on transmission of genes and variation only provides
a basis for divergence by natural selection insofar as it depends
on genotype. Resemblances and differences due merely to the
action of the local environment on the individual are irrelevant
here however interesting and important they may be in other
contexts. The genetics of specific and subspecific differences
have only been investigated experimentally in a few instances
so that the taxonomist's supposition that the characters he
works with are inherited is usually no more than a reasonable
assumption made in the absence of evidence to the contrary.
The recognition that "like begets like" (however untrue in
some genetical situations), and that species have a certain permanence in time due to the conservative forces of inheritance
antedates any clear understanding of genetical mechanisms.

The dark skin color of Africans, for example, was considered to be inherited long before the laws of particulate inheritance were known because African parents, with rare exceptions, have dark-skinned children and because the color is not much changed if they are born and reared in a temperate climate.

The characters that have been used in describing and classifying man from the 18th century until quite recent times have been mainly variations in the size, form, and color of the body and its parts, but the fact that these are bodily variations does not, of course, guarantee that they are solely or even partly determined by genes. In some cultures it was the custom to distort the shape of the skull by artificially applied pressure but even apart from such obvious examples various lines of evidence indicate that changes of environment can produce a certain amount of alteration in skeletal dimensions. In thinking of the effects of environment it should be noted that prenatal as well as postnatal influences must be included. The terms "congenital" and "innate" are not true equivalents of genetical.

Granted that, as human taxonomists, we should be concerned strictly with the distribution patterns of genetical characters it is important to consider what this implies. We may note first that the word *character*, which it is so often convenient to use in discussing these matters, means no more than some property of the organism which we isolate for study. Taking the meaning in this wide sense it is clear that the best characters to use in comparing individuals or populations at the genetical level would be genes themselves; but, as yet, genes cannot be identified individually by direct observation but only by observing their effects. These effects may be many removes from the primary action of the gene and variations due to changes in the gene itself may be more or less obscured by superimposed variations due to environmental factors and to other genes which happen to be present. The geneticist, in short, tries to infer genotypic structure by examining phenotypes. He may study various properties of human beings ranging from skull form to the composition of specific proteins and from color perception to performance in psychological tests. By observing familial resemblances and the pattern of variation in family lines he tries to infer whether genes are involved and if so how many and which ones. The extent to which he can succeed in this analysis depends both on the precision of his methods and on the inherent complexity of the genetical situation.

As we now see the matter, genes are chemical entities with an orderly linear structure by virtue of which they are able to provide coded instructions for the correct synthesis of various proteins or parts of proteins. Although the gene itself does not synthesize the protein directly and several stages involving other substances intervene in the process, it seems that changes in the composition of the protein often reflect very faithfully specific alterations in the genetic code. The inference from the phenotype, in this case the structure of the protein, to the gene is as secure as we can hope to achieve though still perhaps not entirely certain. If, then, we require high precision in the specification of genetical variation it is to chemical studies like those on the inherited variants of human hemoglobin that we must turn.

None of the phenotypic characters used in classical anthropology has been analyzed with anything like the precision which we have come to demand in biochemical genetics and for most of them our genetical knowledge is still in the most rudimentary state. Only too often we still lack satisfactory methods for scoring or measuring them accurately so that precise comparison of either populations or members of families is not possible. Caliper measurements, it is true, have long been in use to describe the size and form of the living body and the skelton, and objective methods for measuring skin and hair color have lately become available; but eye color, the Mongolian epicanthic fold, and the form of the hair still defy accurate treatment. It seems from work on animals and from the little that has been done on man that metrical characters such as stature and skin color, which do not show clear genetical segregation in families, depend on several and perhaps many genes, the effects of which on the phenotype are approximately additive. Statistical methods for analyzing this type of inheritance have been developed for investigation of commercially important qualities in cattle, sheep, and poultry but there are difficulties which limit their application to human material. In the most favorable cases the analysis may yield fairly reliable estimates of the number of genes involved but they still cannot be identified individually. This being so we are in no position to say whether populations which are phenotypically similar in these multifactorial characters are also similar genetically. As we have already mentioned above, certain populations which are widely sep- arated geographically resemble one another in skin color and in various other metrical characters but differ in their fre- quencies of blood groups and other simply inherited traits. This may at least lead us to doubt whether these anatomical resemblances also imply genetical similarity and indicate the need for caution in accepting these resemblances as evidence of a close common ancestry. Detailed genetical analysis of metrical characters is at present not possible but it should be emphasized that it may be by no means easy to distinguish variations due to different mutational events even at the biochemical level. A well-known example is the case of hemoglobin D which was found to comprise three different variants when samples from different regions of the world were submitted to full chemical analysis. The electrophoretic methods which are commonly used in screening for hemo- globin variants were in this case inadequate to reveal the heterogeneity of the material and this is not the only example in biochemical genetics of more powerful methods bringing to light previously unsuspected variation.

It is not surprising that many anthropologists have turned from anthropometry to the study of blood groups and other serological and biochemical traits which offer more reliable and detailed genetical information. So many variations of this kind are now known and their advantages for the exact description and analysis of genetical differences between populations are so clear, that it seems more profitable at present to exploit them to the full rather than risk frustrations in trying to elucidate more complex types of variations. Some geneticists, however, reacting against such exclusive preoccupation with single gene substitutions, have emphasized that many, and perhaps most characteristics which are of high biological value are genetically complex and also that natural selection involves the whole genotype as a coordinated system rather than single loci. This is no doubt true and although it is easier for the experimental geneticist to implement this philosophical approach, there are practical as well as theoretical reasons for investigating complex human characters as best we can. In medicine especially we cannot abandon genetical studies on congenital malformations and susceptibility to various diseases because we find that we are not dealing with simple Mendelian situations. There seems no reason also why more studies on fertility and viability in relation to normal variations such as in stature should not be undertaken, and work of this kind might be more interesting to the evolutionist and perhaps more useful to the physician than much of the anthropometry that has been done so far. If, however, our aim is exact description of population differences at the genetical level and precise investigation of the factors which control gene frequencies, there is no doubt that serological and simple biochemical variations are best suited to our purpose.

One can sympathize with the misgivings of anthropometrists about the the anthropological value of blood groups when the distribution of ABO groups seemed inconsistent with their views on human taxonomy but today we need no longer rely solely on the information provided by a single genetic locus. The objection that regional differences in the frequencies of allelic genes may often have originated by random processes (genetic drift) to which multifactorial characters are not so susceptible has less force now that we are in a position to study variation at many independent loci.

It is a necessary, though seemingly endless, task to catalogue the genetical characteristics of the people of the world and to a large extent our work is still in this preliminary, descriptive phase. Using appropriate statistical techniques we can if we wish use these data to measure the extent of overall genetical divergence between various populations but our ultimate goal must be to understand the biological significance of these differences. Since the processes of evolutionary change are, in general, slow the pattern of variation which we see today must be to some extent the result of events in the remote past about which we can scarcely hope to have direct and detailed evidence. Our explanations are bound to be speculative and the best we can hope is that by accumulating data and combining many sources of evidence they will gradually become more probable.

One result of the urge to classify mankind into discrete racial groups has been a tendency to think of the later phase of human evolution as consisting exclusively of migrations and intermixtures between such groups. It has often been supposed that at some time in the past the human species consisted of more isolated and more clearly differentiated groups and that this simple primeval pattern of variation has been obscured by subsequent movement and hybridization. In its extreme form this trend culminated in the concept of "pure races." The view that earlier populations were substantially less variable than many modern ones of comparable scale has been questioned by many population geneticists and receives little or no support from the study of prehistoric skeletal material. The only sense in which the notion of pure races seems to have any reality is that some populations have been more isolated than others and that gene exchange with other populations has been relatively small at least in the recent past. That genetical differentiation between the populations of major geographical regions could only have occured if gene flow between them was to some extent restricted is an acceptable proposition. It is also true that the growth of populations and development in the means of transport has led to more intermixing, but the intergradations which we find on the map are not necessarily due to this proces alone. It may be, for example, that the gradation reflects the action of graded selective forces on populations that were relatively static. The idea of a race as a discrete unit characterized by a particular complex of physical attributes is harmful if it leads to typological thinking, that is to the conception of an idealized type in which all these characteristics are combined. This way of thinking deflects attention from the essential variability of populations and from the fact that the characters by which the race is defined are usually independent in inheritance and probably to a large extent independent in their responses to selection.

It should be clear from what has already been said above that to speak of a character as genetical is no more than a convenient abbreviation. No character, as has been often said, is solely due to genes or solely due to environment for both are intimately involved in the development and functioning of the organism. Some kinds of variation are attributable almost entirely to changes in genes in the sense that given the appropriate genotype they are manifested in any environmental conditions compatible with life; there are others in which genes play a major but not exclusive part and others still in which the role of genes is minor or negligible. Confronted with a diversity of human differences it is for us to investigate each on its own merits in order to discover to what extent and in what ways genes are involved.

This leads us naturally to the most controversial area in the study of human populations, namely the question of differences in temperament and mental powers. We cannot discuss this matter at length but the interested reader may find it helpful to refer to the writings of Klineberg (1935, 1951), Montagu (1964), Penrose (1963) and Vernon (1960). Probably no one cares very much if he is told that the population to which he belongs has an unusually high frequency of the Rhesus gene Ro but he may be resentful if it is also suggested that it is unusually stupid or indolent especially if it is alleged that these qualities are hereditary. It is true, as we have already pointed out, that animal taxonomists sometimes find aspects of behavior as useful for diagnostic purposes as anatomical differences and it is legitimate to ask why this should not also be the case in man. The customs and rituals which accompany betrothal and marriage vary greatly and may be fairly characteristic of particular societies, but most people would not regard them in the same light as courtship displays in birds or fruitflies. They are not stereotyped forms of behavior which depend to a large extent on genetical constitution but socially approved modes of behavior which are learned afresh in every generation and would rapidly disappear, as many have, as soon as they are no longer taught. The same is true of languages, laws, techniques, forms of political organization and all the other items which go to make up the cultural heritage of a society. While it is true that the particular forms in which cultural achievement manifests itself are

certainly inherited only in a social and not a biological sense
it is still reasonable to ask whether the mental powers on
which cultural achievement depends may not be subject to
genetical variation. If individual capacity to learn and to invent
can be shown to depend to some extent on genes may not
the genes which are involved vary in incidence in different
populations? Geneticists vary greatly in their assessment of the
importance of genetical influences on human mentality as
may be seen for example from the comments on the statement on Race issued by Unesco (1952 *loc. cit.*). Given that
mental functions depend on the brain together with various
physiological factors which influence cerebral activity, it
would certainly be amazing if genetical variability were not
involved. We know of mental disorders attributable to
mutational changes at certain loci or to chromosomal aber-
rations and there are others in which genetical changes play
a less clearly definable part. It seems then that some genetical
abnormalities can lead to mental impairment but the question
that concerns us more closely is the part played by genes in
mental functioning within the "normal" range. Scientific
work on this question has centered largely on intelligence as
measured by various standard tests. Intelligence measured in
this way is a continuous variate like stature and analysis by
orthodox methods of test results on family material indicates
that a substantial part of the variability is attributable to
genetic causes. The magnitude of this genetical component is,
however, open to dispute and the validity of attempts to ap-
portion it have been questioned, for example by Hogben
(1939). Even if the estimates of the genetical component from
studies on subjects reared in a western European type of
culture are acceptable they are not necessarily valid for mankind in general. The reason is that when environmental
sources of variation are minimized by working on a group

which is culturally fairly homogeneous, residual variation is naturally genetical. This however does not exclude the possibility that more extreme differences of environment might exert large effects. When we use our tests to investigate Australian aborigines and other peoples whose indigenous culture is widely different from our own it is often, but not invariably, found that their scores fall below European norms; but unless we believe, as some psychologists have, that our tests measure "innate" or "culture free" intelligence the genetical significance of these results is open to doubt and may in fact be nil. There is probably no form of test which is free from cultural bias. If we could test samples of two populations which were of widely different origins but brought up in identical physical and cultural conditions then difference in their test scores might have more interest to the geneticist; but we could only hope to find these conditions in a society where no "race question" in the social sense existed and the results for such a society would only be of academic interest. Work on American Negroes in circumstances which at least go some way towards the requirements of such an experiment seem to indicate that mean test scores of Negroes and whites become close as educational and other environmental factors become more similar. In both Negroes and whites there is considerable variability of scores around the mean values and much overlapping of the distributions. If some part of the average difference in test scores between populations can be attributed to genetical causes, and this is by no means proved, it seems improbable that it is very large. It must also be remembered that the tests are usually designed to discriminate abilities of Europeans in a European cultural milieu; given other tests and other environmental circumstances it by no means follows that European scores would surpass those of other populations.

References

Allison, A. C. 1961. Genetic factors in resistance to malaria. *Annual New York Academy of Science* 91:710.

Barnicot, N. A. 1964 in press. Anthropology and population genetics. *Proceedings of the XIth International Congress of Genetics*, The Hague, Netherlands.

Biasutti, R. 1953–57. *Razze e popoli della terra*, second ed. Turin, Unione Tipografico.

Burt, W. H. 1954. The subspecies category in mammals. *Systematic Zoology* 3:99.

Cain, A. J. 1954. *Animal Species and Their Evolution*. London, Hutchinson.

Cavalli-Sforza, L. L. and A. W. F. Edwards. 1964 in press. Analysis of human evolution. *Proceedings of the XIth International Congress of Genetics*. The Hague, Netherlands.

Deniker, J. 1900. *The Races of Man*. London, Walter Scott Ltd.

Dice, Lee R. 1940. Ecologic and genetic variability within species of *Peromyscus*. *American Naturalist* 74:212.

Dobzhansky, T. 1951. *Genetics and the Origin of Species*, third ed. New York, Columbia University Press.

Eickstedt, E. F. von. 1937. *Rassengeschichte und der Menschheit*. Stuggart, Ferdinand Enke.

Haddon, A. C. 1924. *The Races of Man and Their Distribution*. Cambridge, Cambridge University Press.

Hogben, Lancelot. 1939. *Nature and Nurture*. London, Allen & Unwin.

Huxley, T. H. 1865. On the methods and results of ethnology. In *Man's Place in Nature and Other Anthropological Essays*. London, Macmillan Co., 1894.

Klineberg, Otto. 1935. *Race Differences*. New York, Harper & Bros.

———. 1951. *Race and Psychology. The Race Question in Modern Science*. Paris, UNESCO.

Livingstone, Frank. 1962. On the non-existence of human races. *Current Anthropology* 3:279.

Mayr, E. 1942. *Systematics and the Origin of Species*. New York, Columbia University Press.

Montagu, M. F. Ashley. 1964. *Man's Most Dangerous Myth: The Fallacy of Race*, fourth ed. New York, World Publishing Co.

Morant, G. M. 1939. *The Races of Central Europe: A Footnote to History*. London, George Allen & Unwin Ltd.

Penrose, L. S. 1952. The Race Concept: Results of an Enquiry. *The Race Question in Modern Science*. Paris, UNESCO.

Penrose, L. S. 1963. *The Biology of Mental Defect*, third ed. London, Sedgwick & Jackson.

Simpson, G. G. 1961. *Principles of Animal Taxonomy*. New York, Columbia University Press.

Sneath, P. H. A. 1961. Recent developments in theoretical and quantitative taxonomy. *Systematic Zoology* 10:118.

Topinard, Paul. 1878. *Anthropology*. London, Chapman & Hall.

Vallois, Henri V. 1943. *Anthropologie de la population francaise*. Didier, Toulouse & Paris.

Various authors. 1962. A Survey of some genetical characters in Ethiopian tribes. *American Journal of Physical Anthropology* 20: 168.

Vernon, Philip E. 1960. *Race and intelligence*. In *Man, Race and Darwin*. Oxford University Press.

Washburn, S. L. 1963. The Study of Race. *American Anthropologist* 65:521.

Wilson, E. O. and W. L. Brown. 1953. The subspecies concept and its taxonomic application. *Systematic Zoology* 2:97.

X   On Coon's *The Origin of Races*

ASHLEY MONTAGU

A current example of the kind of thinking about race which is criticized by the various contributors to the present volume is represented by Dr. Carleton S. Coon's *The Origin of Races* (1962). In this volume Dr. Coon sets out to reconstruct the origin of human races, developing the view postulated by the late Dr. Franz Weidenreich that, since "human forms preceding those of modern man were distributed over the entire Old World, and differed typically from each other," it ought to be possible to trace back, at least, some of the living races to their remote ancestors. A bold, but alas, impossible task, since the relevant available knowledge is quite insufficient to enable us to trace the origins of even the most closely related living populations, or satisfactorily to demonstrate their genetic relationships. The necessary facts are simply not available. This sobering fact has deterred less imaginative anthropologists than Dr. Coon from attempting such daring reconstructions. In the absence of the necessary facts, speculation can be the golden guess to the full round of truth. Dr. Coon conjectures and theorizes on the basis of such facts as are available—a perfectly legiti-

Rewritten and reprinted from *Current Anthropology*, Vol. 4, No. 4, October, 1963, pp. 361–364.

mate procedure. Theory is the life-blood of science, and the value of a theory lies not so much in whether it is ultimately proven to be true or false, but in its fruitfulness. Coon has presented a theory of the origin of human races. That theory will be critically examined here.

Coon's theory, in his own words, is "that at the beginning of our record, over half a million years ago, man was a single species, *Homo erectus*, perhaps already divided into five geographic races or subspecies. *Homo erectus* then evolved into *Homo sapiens* not once but five times, as each subspecies, living in its own territory, passed a critical threshold from a more brutal to a more sapient state" (p. 656).

As a matter of interest, it would be helpful to know on what grounds Coon assumes that his assumed five subspecies of *Homo erectus* were "more brutal" than their descendants of the *sapient* state. "Brutal" is a word capable of several meanings in such a context, and when juxtaposed to "sapient" perpetuates pejorative and odious comparisons which are of questionable validity in scientific or any other discussions. If Coon means by "more brutal" that *Homo erectus* in his various morphological forms was different or less evolved than *Homo sapiens*, it may be suggested that "brutal" is not the best word with which to convey that idea.

The idea that five subspecies or geographic races of *Homo erectus*, in isolation from one another, "evolved independently into *Homo sapiens* not once but five times" at different times and in different places, is so far-fetched, that it is surprising to find it being proposed at all. It is far-fetched because it is quite out of harmony with the biological facts. Species and subspecies simply don't develop that way. As Dr. Theodosius Dobzhansky has remarked in connection with Coon's theory, "The specific unity of mankind was maintained throughout its history by gene flow due to migrations and the

process for which the word 'genosorption'[1] is suggested. . . .
Excepting through such gene flow, repeated origins of the
same species are so improbable that this conjecture is not
worthy of serious consideration; and given a gene flow, it
becomes fallacious to say that a species has originated repeatedly, and even more fallacious to contend that it has originated five times, or any other number above one" (1963). And
as Dr. D. F. Roberts has pointed out,

Mutations occur and, over a long period, by selection new more
favourable mutant genes accumulate, which from their random
origin are very unlikely to be similar in the different lines, the
more so the longer the lines have been separated. It is this process
that leads to species differentiation both in time and space, brought
about by the diversification and subsequent fixation of different
alleles at a sufficient number of loci to seriously reduce, if not
eliminate, compatibility of the gene complexes of any male of one
species mating with any female of another. Coon suggests that
there occurred five times independently similar sequences of mutations, that there became established five times similar sequences
of mutants, sequences so long as to result in chronological speciation but so similar as to allow continued interfertility between the
lines. To the reviewer [Roberts] this view appears so highly improbable as to merit the scantest of attention (1963).

Quite independently the same point is made by Dr. John W.
Crenshaw, Jr., who writes, "The parallel evolution of the races
of man suggested by Coon hardly have been independent in
the sense that the genotypes responsible for the *sapiens* phenotype occurred as novel gene combinations independently in
the different races of men. This would constitute an improb-
ability of remarkable magnitude" (1963). It is true that the
evolutionary process is an agency through which the improbable is maximized, but neither in the evolutionary facts nor in
the theoretical considerations involved, is there to be found

---

1. Genosorption: the incorporation of the genes of one population into
the gene pool of another.

any probability that the same species evolved five different times. Granting the very doubtful proposition that *Homo erectus* was in fact a species separate from *Homo sapiens*, the evolution of one species into another is a very gradual process, and the development of the subspecies reflects the development of the species as a whole. However few or many so-called subspecies of *Homo erectus* there may have been, all of them, at one time or another, probably participated in the development of the form of man we call *sapiens*. What peculiar forces could there have been at work to have produced so many different subspecies from a single species and then uniquely transformed them, one at a time and in different geographic areas, into a different single species? It is a rhetorical question, for there never were such peculiar forces at work, except in Dr. Coon's fecund imagination. In fact, if Coon's argument were sound it would be expected that the independent subspecies, as incipient species, would have tended to develop in the direction of becoming different species, and this we know never to have occurred. But as Coon's theory stands, were it in any way sound, the living so-called races or subspecies of man would present the most remarkable example of parallel or convergent evolution in the history of animated nature.

The species *Homo sapiens* is a species because all its members have shared a more or less common biological history—allowing for all the differences in that history which each population or so-called race or subspecies has undergone. Coon implies that that history has been essentially and independently different for his five assumed races, and further implies that in isolation the genetic direction of *Homo erectus* was predetermined, that each of the subspecies hidden away in their little ecological niches would inevitably have developed into *sapiens*. But the evolutionary process, as we have learned to understand it, even for man the cultural creature, does not work like that, as is abundantly testified by such of his biological history as we understand of man himself. For if the so-called subspecies of man had developed in the kind of independent isolation Coon postulates, they would have exhibited —owing, among other things, to the inherent variability of man's genetic constitution—far greater differences in their earlier and more recent forms than they, in fact, do.

What is so remarkable about the varieties of man is their likenesses, not their differences. It would be demanding too much of any theory to require it to make out a case for an independent and parallel and convergent evolution of varieties of any kind as like one another as are the so-called races of man.

Coon's book, judged in the perspective of anthropological history, would represent yet another of those ambitious attempts which are periodically made to unravel the tangled skein of man's biological history, and it could be written off as no more successful than the previous attempts have been, were it not for the fact that Coon delivers himself of opinions as if they were oracular and of fancies as if they were facts. Since so many of the statements he makes are both unsound and misleading, and have already been misused by racists without the slightest disavowal and repudiation from him of the uses to which his views have been put, the further critical examination of his ideas may serve to illustrate the dangers and the inadequacies of the kind of thinking represented by Dr. Coon's book.

From the very first page of his book Coon makes statements of the following kind: "Each major race had followed a pathway of its own through the labyrinth of time. Each had been molded in a different fashion to meet the needs of different environments, and each had reached its own level on the evolutionary scale" (p. vii). The assumption is clear here: The races of man occupy different levels on the evolutionary ladder (for that is what "scale" actually means in this context and in literal translation), some are "higher" and some are "lower" than others in that "scale." Coon does not speak of "higher" and "lower" races, but that is the implication of his quoted statement and the obvious inference to be drawn from it, namely, that "higher" and "lower" races of man stand at different levels on the evolutionary ladder or scale.[2] This is a promising beginning, and if there can be any doubt as to Coon's meaning at this point, he leaves us in none as he proceeds.

Coon regrets that "dead men can take no intelligence tests," the implication being that if they could significant differences in their IQs would be revealed. Some of us, however, may heave a sigh of relief that intelligence tests have not been added to the other terrors of death. Coon, apparently, has more faith in intelligence tests, especially when applied cross-culturally or racially, than most experts have. In the light of what is to come, this is not surprising. "However," he goes on to say, "it is a fair inference that fossil men now extinct were less gifted than their descendants who have larger brains, that the subspecies that crossed the evolutionary threshold into the category of *Homo sapiens* the earliest have evolved the most, and that the obvious correlation between the length of time a subspecies has been in the *sapiens* state and the levels of civilization attained by some of its populations may be related phenomena" (pp. ix–x).

I confess none of this makes sense to me. In the matter of brains: Was Neanderthal man with a mean cranial capacity of 1,550cc brighter than contemporary white men with a mean cranial capacity of 1,400cc? If not, then why should we be any more gifted than many of our extinct ancestors with smaller brains than ours? I altogether fail to see why a sub-

---

2. From the Latin *scala,* a ladder or flight of steps, an 18th-century gradational concept, the "échelle des êtres," "the ladder or scale of being" of so many 18th-century writers.

species—granting the very doubtful proposition that it is a
subspecies—which has been in the *sapiens* state longer than
another subspecies has evolved the most and is obviously going
to have a higher level of civilization. In the zone of adaptation
in which man lives, the cultural dimension, cultural or social
time plays havoc with arguments of development based on
secular time (Sorokin 1943; Montagu 1938). The accident of
geography alone may enable one population to pack more
experience into fifty years than others living in less favorable
areas would be able to do in five, or for that matter, in fifty
thousand years. The differences in the history of experience
undergone by different peoples is, surely, the major factor determining the differences in cultural development that they
present? But Coon prefers the biologistic interpretation represented by these cultural differences, "the level on the evolutionary scale" occupied, according to him, by the living
"races" of mankind, is correlated with "the levels of civilization attained by some of" these populations.

Since, according to Coon, the Negroes were the last of the
subspecies of *Homo erectus* to be transformed into *sapiens*
(pp. 655–656), the level of civilization attained by them is "explained." They simply do not have as long a biological or
genetic history as *sapiens*, as we whites or Causasoids, and, interestingly enough, as the so-called archaic Australoids (who
should be very advanced, but strangely enough, are not), so
it is not to be wondered at that we are as *we* are, and they are
as *they* are. Should the reader of Coon's treatise wish to see
what one of the earliest (according to Coon) *sapientes* looks
like in relation to one of the last (again, according to Coon),
photographic reproductions are provided for him, on Plate 32
opposite p. 371. Here he will see an Australian aboriginal
woman pictured above, and a Chinese scientist pictured below.
The caption reads: "The Alpha and Omega of *Homo sapiens:*
An Australian aboriginal woman with a cranial capacity of un-

der 1,000cc (Topsy, a Tiwi); and a Chinese sage with a brain nearly twice that size (Dr. Li Chi, the renowned archaeologist and director of Academia Sinica)." "An Australian aboriginal woman" and "a Chinese sage." How does Dr. Coon know that Dr. Li is a sage? Does being an archaeologist make him so? Or does the apposition of "aboriginal" and "sage" serve to make a point? "Alpha and Omega," the first and the last. "Obviously" Topsy just "growed," and is what she is, a poor benighted Australian aboriginal, principally because she has a small brain, and Dr. Li is principally what he is because he has a large brain. Of course, there are cultural differences, but the implication is that no matter what cultural advantages Topsy and her children had been afforded, neither she nor they could have accomplished what Dr. Li has achieved.

Coon nowhere produces the slightest evidence in support of his statement that Topsy had a cranial capacity of "under 1,000cc." It is extremely unlikely that Topsy had a cranial capacity of "under 1,000cc." Klaatsch, in his famous study of the Australian aboriginal skull, turned up none with so small a cranial capacity (1908). I know of no studies on the cranial capacity of the aborigines of Bathurst and Melville Islands, the homelands of the Tiwi. The nearest Australian aborigines of Northern Australia have, however, been studied in this connection, and von Bonin found the average cranial capacity to be 1,256cc (1934; Hambly 1947). We shall await with interest Coon's documentation of Topsy's "under 1,000cc" cranial capacity. But whether Coon documents this statement or not it is surely both unfair and unscientific to compare cranial capacities of two individuals from two different groups, and then proceed to draw conclusions from such a comparison for the groups as a whole. The citation of averages and their statistical variance would have been somewhat more meaningful, even though that meaningfulness would be limited to the clearer statement of the variation in cranial capacity characterizing the two groups. For the rest, such comparisons are meaningless, except in the service of such theories as Coon offers in *The Origin of Races*.

Apart from the demonstrable fallacies involved in cranial capacity comparisons, it surely does not have to be restated once more that brain size, within the normal range of variation characteristic for the human species at the *sapiens* level, and characteristic also of every human population, has nothing whatever to do with intelligence. A cranial capacity of 850cc in a perfectly normal European is occasionally encountered (Hechst 1932), in a land area in which one may also encounter an Anatole France with a brain size no larger than Topsy's. Anatole France's brain weighed 1,017 grams, and there was some atrophy of the right cerebral hemisphere, yet in spite of this small brain size and senile atrophic changes he maintained his brilliance to the last (Guillaume-Louis 1927). But what interests me is why Dr. Coon, who thinks so little of Negroes, should have failed to make any reference to such earlier Negroid peoples as the so-called Boskopoids, with cranial capacities in the vicinity of 1,700cc. Or why not go the whole hog and make reference to the Zitzikama Negroid with a cranial capacity of 1,925cc? The answer, of course, is that such facts do not suit Dr. Coon's argument.

According to Coon the Australian aborigines "come closest, of any living peoples, to the *erectus-sapiens* threshold" (p. 427). Therefore they ought to be "less gifted" according to Coon than ourselves and the large-brained Mongoloids. And, of course (but Coon does not add this), the large-brained Mongoloids, having larger brains than Caucasoids, ought to be "more gifted" than ourselves.

Coon tells us that "The genetic basis for high intelligence has been acquired independently in different taxonomic categories of primates. There is no evidence that the most successful populations within several different human races have not also become bright independently" (p. 184). In other words, the probabilities are high that there exists a "genetic basis for high intelligence" in these different populations. So far as Coon is concerned Dobzhansky and Montagu need never have written their paper on "Natural Selection and the Mental Capacities of Mankind" (1947), in which the theory is set forth that the mental capacities of the different populations of mankind were probably much-of-a-muchness because in the evolution of every human population much the same behavioral traits had been at a premium. But this is not an idea congenial to Coon's theory. Coon finds also that human beings vary in temperament. "It is a common observation among anthropologists who have worked in many parts of the world in intimate contact with people of different races that racial differences in temperament also exist and can be predicted" (p. 116). This is news to me. I had been under the impression that the common observation among anthropologists had been that the more one got to know "people of different races" the more fundamentally alike they appeared to be beneath the surface of the superficial differences. I had also been under the impression that this had constituted one of the principal contributions made by anthropology to the understanding of man. But apparently there is a lock upon some people's understanding.

The African Negroes—Coon's "Congoids"—would almost seem to have been specially created, according to Coon's "findings." "As far as we know now," he writes, "the Congoid line started on the same evolutionary level as the Eurasiatic ones in the Early Middle Pleistocene and then stood still for half a million years, after which Negroes and Pygmies appeared as if out of nowhere" (p. 658). Of course, the joker in the pack lies in the "As far as we know now." And what we know now does not take us very far. Indeed, it is precisely so little that the half million years of standing still opined by Coon represents nothing more than the standstill before our abysmal lack of knowledge concerning the Negro's physical evolution. As Birdsell has stated, "There is virtually no fossil evidence pertinent to the antiquity of the Negroid peoples of Africa . . . there is no reason to assume that they have evolved suddenly and late into *sapiens* form. Negative evidence simply cannot be used for such conclusions" (1963). In any event, according to Coon, the top-drawer peoples did not originate in the Dark Continent. The Children of Light originated elsewhere. "If Africa was the cradle of mankind," we are told, "it was only an indifferent kindergarten. Europe and Asia were our principal schools" (p. 656). And, of course, the Negroes have remained in kindergarten ever since, but we Caucasoids have gone on to more advanced institutions.

"Genes in a population," Coon tells us, "are in equilibrium if the population is living a healthy life as a corporate entity. Racial intermixture can upset the genetic as well as the social equilibrium of a group, and so, newly introduced genes tend to disappear or to be reduced to a minimum percentage unless they possess a selective advantage over their local counterparts" (p. 661).

The population genetics of these statements are entirely erroneous and, so far from reflecting facts, the truth is that under favorable conditions newly introduced genes can establish themselves very rapidly, especially within a small breeding population. As for racial intermixture upsetting the genetic equilibrium of a group, the evidence of everyday experience throughout the world and of field investigations is entirely contrary to this statement. Human hybrids tend to show greater resistance to disease, and increase in fertility, probably due to the combined slight heterotic effects of many individual genes (King 1961). And, as Penrose has shown, it is also probable that the levels of intelligence are not only prevented from declining as a result of hybridization, but are refreshed and enhanced by the introduction of new genes (Penrose 1955).

To say that Dr. Coon's knowledge of genetics is peculiar is perhaps an understatement. *"Recombination,"* he tells us, "known as Mendel's second law, is the process by which rows of gene-molecules strung together on chromosomes break up and form new associations" (p. 21). The law to which Dr. Coon refers is better known as the law of independent assortment, and refers to the behavior of two or more pairs of alleles carried on different chromosomes, and the separation of each pair of chromosomes into different gametes independently of other pairs. The result is that the gametes contain all possible combinations of the genes constituting the different pairs. What Coon describes is not this but crossing-over, the exchange of material between homologous chromosomes at meiosis.

Then there is the fundamental proposition, fundamental for Coon's argument, that "Although the component populations of a polytypic species evolve as a unit, they cannot do so simultaneously since it takes time for a mutation to spread from one population to another" (p. 29). The component populations of a polytypic species not only can but usually do evolve "as a unit," since mutations occur in all the polytypes of the species, and the gene flow between the polytypes has been more or less considerable.

Finally, Coon announces that had it "been in the evolutionary scheme of things, and had it not been advantageous to each of the geographical races for it to retain, for the most part, the adaptive elements in its genetic *"status quo"* we would all have been "homogenized" by now (p. 662).

What Coon seems to have failed to understand in this book is that what he takes to be "the evolutionary scheme of things" represents no more than his rather confused view of very difficult problems which his book has only served to render more confused. If anything, the reader is confused on a lower level than he was before. "The evolutionary scheme of things" is not some mystical process which has kept men apart from one another, from being "homogenized," to use Coon's exceedingly unpleasant word. The evolutionary process has no scheme, and it has not schemed to keep men apart for adaptive or any other reasons. What has kept men apart have been physiographic and social barriers, principally the former, and this is why the so-called "geographical races," being separated by geography and a variety of similar barriers, have not been, to use Coon's unfortunate word, "homogenized."

References

Birdsell, J. S. 1963. The origin of human races. *The Quarterly Review of Biology* 38:178–185.

Coon, C. S. 1962. *The Origin of Races.* New York, Knopf.

Crenshaw, J. W., Jr. 1963. Direction of human evolution: a zoologist's view. *Human Biology* 35:250–262.

Dobzhansky, Th. 1963. Genetic entities in human evolution. In S. L. Washburn (Editor), *Classification and Human Evolution.* Viking Fund Publications in Anthropology 37:347–362.

Dobzhansky, Th. and A. Montagu. 1947. Natural se ?ction and the mental capacities of mankind. *Science* 105:587–590.

Guillaume-Louis, P. 1927. Le cerveau d'Anatole France. *Revue International de Médecine et Chirurgie* 38:146–150.

Hambly, W. D. 1947. Cranial capacity, a study in methods. *Fieldiana —Anthropology.* Chicago Natural History Museum 36:25–75.

Hechst, B. 1932. Über einen Fall von Mikroencephalie ohne Geistigen Defekt. *Archiv für Psychiatrie und Nervenkrankheiten* 57: 64–76.

King, J. C. 1961. Inbreeding, heterosis and information therapy. *American Naturalist* 95:345–364.

Klaatsch, H. 1908. The skull of the Australian aboriginal. *Reports From the Pathological Laboratory of the Lunacy Department of New South Wales* 1:43–167.

Montagu, A. 1938. Social time: a methodological and functional analysis. *American Journal of Sociology* 24:282–284.

Penrose, L. S. 1955. Evidence of heterosis in man. *Proceedings of the Royal Society* 144:203–213.

Roberts, D. F. 1963. Review of *The Origin of Races. Human Biology* 35:443–445.

Sorokin, P. A. 1943. *Sociocultural Causality, Space, Time.* Durham, N.C., Duke University Press.

von Bonin, G. 1934. On the size of man's brain, as indicated by skull capacity. *Journal of Comparative Neurology* 59:1–28.

XI   The Study of Race

S. L. WASHBURN

Discussion of the races of man seems to generate endless emotion and confusion. I am under no illusion that this paper can do much to dispel the confusion; it may add to the emotion. The latest information available supports the traditional findings of anthropologists and other social scientists—that there is no scientific basis of any kind for racial discrimination. I think that the way this conclusion has been reached needs to be restated. The continuation of antiquated biological notions in anthropology and the oversimplification of facts weakens the anthropological position. We must realize that great changes have taken place in the study of race over the last 20 years and it is up to us to bring our profession into the forefront of the newer understandings, so that our statements will be authoritative and useful.

This paper will be concerned with three topics—the modern concept of race, the interpretation of racial differences, and the social significance of race. And, again, I have no illusion that these things can be treated briefly; I shall merely say a few things which are on my mind and which you may

Delivered as the Presidential address at the Annual Meeting of the American Anthropological Association, November 16, 1962, in Chicago. Reprinted from *American Anthropologist*, Vol. 65, No. 3, June, 1963.

amplify by turning to the literature, and especially to Dob-zhansky's book, *Mankind Evolving*. This book states the relations between culture and genetics in a way which is useful to social scientists. In my opinion it is a great book which puts the interrelations of biology and culture in proper perspective and avoids the oversimplifications which come from overemphasis on either one alone.

The races of man are the result of human evolution, of the evolution of our species. The races are open parts of the species, and the species is a closed system. If we look, then, upon long-term human evolution, our first problem must be the species and the things which have caused the evolution of all mankind, not the races, which are the result of local forces and which are minor in terms of the evolution of the whole species. (A contrary view has recently been expressed by Coon in *The Origin of Races*. I think that great antiquity of human races is supported neither by the record nor by evolutionary theory.)

The evolution of races is due, according to modern genetics, to mutation, selection, migration, and genetic drift. It is easy to shift from this statement of genetic theory to complications of hemoglobin, blood groups, or other technical information. But the point I want to stress is that the primary implication of genetics for anthropology is that it affirms the relation of culture and biology in a far firmer and more important way than ever in our history before. Selection is for reproductive success, and in man reproductive success is primarily determined by the social system and by culture. Effective behavior is the question, not something else.

Drift depends on the size of population, and population size, again, is dependent upon culture, not upon genetic factors as such. Obviously, migration depends on clothes, transportation, economy, and warfare, and is reflected in the archeological record. Even mutation rates are now affected by technology.

Genetic theory forces the consideration of culture as the major factor in the evolution of man. It thus reaffirms the fundamental belief of anthropologists that we must study man both as a biological and as a social organism. This is no longer a question of something that might be desirable; it must be done if genetic theory is correct.

We have, then, on the one hand the history of genetic systems, and on the other hand the history of cultural systems, and, finally, the interrelation between these two. There is no evolution in the traditional anthropological sense. What Boas referred to as evolution was orthogenesis—which receives no support from modern genetic theory. What the geneticist sees as evolution is far closer to what Boas called history than to what he called evolution, and some anthropologists are still fighting a nineteenth-century battle in their presentation of evolution. We have, then, the history of cultural systems, which you may call history; and the history of genetic systems, which you may call evolution if you want to, but if you use this word remember that it means selection, migration, drift—it is real history that you are talking about and not some mystic force which constrains mankind to evolve according to some orthogenetic principle.

There is, then, no possibility of studying human raciation, the process of race formation, without studying human culture. Archeology is as important in the study of the origin of races as is genetics; all we can do is reconstruct as best we can the long-term past, and this is going to be very difficult.

Now let me contrast this point of view with the one which has been common in much of anthropology. In the first place, anthropology's main subject, the subject of race, disregarded to an amazing degree the evolution of the human species. Anthropologists were so concerned with the subdivisions within our species and with minor detailed differences between small parts of the species that the physical anthropologists largely forgot that mankind is a species and that the important thing is the evolution of this whole group, not the minor differences between its parts.

If we look back to the time when I was educated, races were regarded as types. We were taught to go to a population and divide it into a series of types and to re-create history out of this artificial arrangement. Those of you who have read *Current Anthropology* will realize that this kind of anthropology is still alive, amazingly, and in full force in some countries; relics of it are still alive in our teaching today.

Genetics shows us that typology must be completely removed from our thinking if we are to progress. For example, let us take the case of the Bushmen. The Bushmen have been described as the result of a mixture between Negro and Mongoloid. Such a statement could only be put in the literature without any possible consideration of migration routes, of numbers of people, of cultures, of any way that such a mixing could actually take place. The fact is that the Bushmen had a substantial record in South Africa and in East Africa and there is no evidence that they ever were anywhere else except in these areas. In other words, they are a race which belongs exactly where they are.

If we are concerned with history let us consider, on the one hand, the ancestors of these Bushmen 15,000 years ago and the area available to them, to their way of life, and, on the other hand, the ancestors of Europeans at the same time in the area available to them, with their way of life. We will find that the area available to the Bushmen was at least twice that available to the Europeans. The Bushmen were living in a land of optimum game; the Europeans were living close to an ice sheet. There were perhaps from three to five times as many

Bushmen ancestors as there were European ancestors only 15,000 years ago.

If one were to name a major race, or a primary race, the Bushmen have a far better claim in terms of the archeological record than the Europeans. During the time of glacial advance more than half of the Old World available to man for life was in Africa. The numbers and distributions that we think of as normal and the races whose last results we see today are relics of an earlier and far different time in human history.

There are no three primary races, no three major groups. The idea of three primary races stems from nineteenth-century typology; it is totally misleading to put the black-skinned people of the world together—to put the Australian in the same grouping with the inhabitants of Africa. And there are certainly at least three independent origins of the small, dark people, the Pygmies, and probably more than that. There is no single Pygmy race.

If we look to real history we will always find more than three races, because there are more than three major areas in which the raciation of our species was taking place.

If we attempt to preserve the notion of three races, we make pseudo-typological problems. Take for example, again, the problem of the aboriginal Australian. If we have only three races, either they must be put with the people of Africa, with which they have nothing in common, or they must be accounted for by mixture, and in books appearing even as late as 1950, a part of the aboriginal Australian population is described as European, and listed with the Europeans, and the residue is listed with the Africans and left there.

The concept of race is fundamentally changed if we actually look for selection, migration, and study people as they are (who they are, where they are, how many they are); and the majority of anthropological textbooks need substantial revision along these lines.

Since races are open systems which are intergrading, the number of races will depend on the purpose of the classification. This is, I think, a tremendously important point. It is significant that as I was reviewing classifications in preparing this lecture, I found that almost none of them mentioned any purpose for which people were being classified. Race isn't very important biologically. If we are classifying races in order to understand human history, there aren't many human races, and there is very substantial agreement as to what they are. There are from six to nine races, and this difference in number is very largely a matter of definition. These races occupied the major separate geographical areas in the Old World.

If one has no purpose for classification, the number of races can be multiplied almost indefinitely, and it seems to me that the erratically varying number of races is a source of confusion to student, to layman, and to specialist. I think we should require people who propose a classification of races to state in the first place why they wish to divide the human species and to give in detail the important reasons for subdividing our whole species. If important reasons for such classification are given, I think you will find that the number of races is always exceedingly small.

If we consider these six or nine geographical races and the factors which produced them, I think the first thing we want to stress is migration.

All through human history, where we have any evidence of that history, people have migrated. In a recent *Anthropologist* there is a suggestion that it took 400,000 years for a gene that mutated in China to reach Europe. We know, historically, that Alexander the Great went from Greece into Northern India. We know that Mongol tribes migrated from Asia into Europe. Only a person seeking to believe that the races are very separate could possibly believe such a figure as that cited.

Migration has always been important in human history and there is no such thing as human populations which are completely separated from other human populations. And migration necessarily brings in new genes, necessarily reduces the differences between the races. For raciation to take place, then, there must be other factors operating which create difference. Under certain circumstances, in very small populations, differences may be created by genetic drift, or because the founders are for chance reasons very different from other members of the species.

However, the primary factor in the creation of racial differences in the long term is selection. This means that the origin of races must depend on adaptation and that the differences between the races which we see must in times past have been adaptive. I stress the question of time here, bcause it is perfectly logical to maintain that in time past a shovel-shaped incisor, for example, was more efficient than an incisor of other forms and that selection would have been for this, and at the same time to assert that today this dental difference is of absolutely no social importance. It is important to make this point because people generally take the view that something is always adaptive or never adaptive, and this is a fundamental oversimplification of the facts.

Adaptation is always within a given situation. There is no such thing as a gene which has a particular adaptive value; it has this value only under set circumstances. For example, the sickle-cell gene, if Allison and others are right, protects against malaria. This is adaptive if there is malaria, but if there is not malaria it is not adaptive. The adaptive value of the gene, then, is dependent on the state of medicine and has no absolute value. The same is true of the other characteristics associated with race.

I would like to go over some of the suggestions which have been made about the adaptive values of various structures in human beings, because I think these need to be looked at again.

I have stressed that the concept of race which comes from population genetics is compatible with what anthropologists have thought. I think that this concept represents great progress. But when I read the descriptions of the importance of adaptive characteristics, I am not sure that there has been any progress since the nineteenth century.

In this connection I should like to speak for a moment on the notion that the Mongoloids are a race which are adapted to live in the cold, that these are arctic-adapted people.

In the first place, in marked contrast to animals which are adapted to live in the arctic, large numbers of Mongoloids are living in the hot, moist tropics. Altogether unlike animal adaptation, then, the people who are supposed to be adapted to the cold aren't living under cold conditions, and I think we should stress this. For thousands of years the majority of this group have not been living under the conditions which are supposed to have produced them. They are presumed, as an arctic-adapted group following various laws, to have short extremities, flat noses, and to be stocky in build. They are, we might say, as stocky as the Scotch, as flat-nosed as the Norwegians, and as blonde as the Eskimos. Actually, there is no correlation, that is, none that has been well worked out, to support the notion that any of these racial groups is cold-adapted.

Let me say a few more words on this lack of correlation. If one follows the form of the nose, in Europe, as one moves north, narrow noses are correlated with cold climate; in Eastern Asia low noses are correlated with cold climate. In neither case is there the slightest evidence that the difference in the form of the nose has anything whatsoever to do with warming the air that comes into the face. Further, if we look at these differences expressed in this way, we see that they are posed in terms of nineteenth-century notions of what a face is all about.

Let us look at it differently. The nose is the center of a face. Most of a face is concerned with teeth, and bones, and muscles that have to do with chewing. The Mongoloid face is primarily the result of large masseter muscles and the bones from which these muscles arise (malar and gonial angles). This is a complex structural pattern related to the teeth, and a superficially very similar pattern may be seen in the Bushman, whose facial form can hardly be attributed to adaptation to cold.

The face of the Neanderthal man has recently been described also as cold-adapted, though it does not have the characteristics of the Mongoloid face. We are told that the blood supply to the Neanderthal face was greatly increased because the infraorbital foramen was large, bringing more blood to the front of the face. In actual fact, most of the blood to our face does not go through that artery. The artery that carries most of the blood to the face comes along the outside, and even our arteries are far too large to go through the mental or infraorbital foramen of Neanderthal man. This kind of statement, as well as the statement that the maxillary sinus warmed the air and that the function of a large orbit was to keep the eyes from freezing, seems to me an extraordinary retrogression to the worst kind of evolutionary speculation— speculation that antedates genetics and reveals a lack of any kind of reasonable understanding of the structure of the human face.

The point I wish to stress is that those who have spoken of the cold-adaptation of the Mongoloid face and of the Neanderthal face do not know the structure of the human face. We have people writing about human faces who are anatomically illiterate. I am genetically illiterate. I do not know about the hemoglobins. I am not asserting that all of us should be required to be literate in all branches of physical anthropology. As Stanley Garn points out, the field has become complicated, but people who are writing about the structure of the human face should learn the elements of anatomy.

The adaptive value of skin color has been repeatedly claimed, but recently Blum has indicated that the situation is more complicated than it appeared. In the first place, he points out the melanin in the skin doesn't do what anthropologists have said it has done. The part of the skin which mainly stops ultraviolet light, the short-wave length light, is a thickened *stratum corneum*, rather than melanin.

Again, the chimpanzee and the gorilla live in precisely the same climatic conditions in Uganda, but the gorilla has one of the blackest, most deeply pigmented skins of the primates and the chimpanzee has a very light skin. It simply is not true that skin color closely parallels climate. The point here is that racial classification tells us very little. The classification poses problems; it does not solve them.

In scientific method, as I see it, one looks at relevant data and when these data are laid out, as in, say, the classification of races, one may then find a correlation which is helpful. But after that, one has to do an experiment; one has to do something that shows that the correlation has validity. And it's no use continuing to correlate nose-form or skin color with climate. The crude correlations were made many years ago, and to advance the study of race requires new methods and more sophisticated analyses.

When I was a student, there were naive racial interpretations based on the metrical data. When these became unacceptable politically the same people used naive constitutional correlations to reach the same conclusions of social importance. Today we have naive concepts of adaptation, taking

the place of the earlier interpretations, and a recrudescence of
the racial thinking.

All along the line there have been valid problems in race,
valid problems in constitution, and valid problems in adaptation. What I am protesting against strongly is the notion that
one can simply take a factor, such as a high cheekbone, think
that it might be related to climate, and then jump to this conclusion without any kind of connecting link between the two
elements—without any kind of experimental verification of
the sort of material that is being dealt with. If we took really
seriously this notion that a flat face with large maxillary
sinuses, deep orbits, and big brow ridges is cold-adapted, it is
clear that the most cold-adapted animal in the primates is the
gorilla.

Race, then, is a useful concept only if one is concerned
with the kind of anatomical, genetic, and structural differences
which were in time past important in the origin of races. Race
in human thinking is a very minor concept. It is entirely worth
while to have a small number of specialists, such as myself,
who are concerned with the origin of gonial angles, the form
of the nose, the origin of dental patterns, changes in blood-
group frequencies, and so on. But this is a very minor, specialized kind of knowledge.

If classification is to have a purpose, we may look backward to the explanation of the differences between people—
structural, anatomical, physiological differences—and then the
concept of race is useful, but it is useful under no other circumstances, as far as I can see.

When the meaning of skin color and structure is fully
understood, it will help us to understand the origin of races,
but this is not the same thing as understanding the origin of
our species. It will help in the understanding of why color
was important in time long past, but it will have no meaning
to modern technical society.

I turn now to a brief statement on the influence of culture upon race. Beginning with agriculture and continuing at an ever-increasing rate, human customs have been interposed between the organism and the environment. The increase of our species from perhaps as few as five million before agriculture to three billion today is the result of new technology, not of biological evolution. The conditions under which the races evolved are mainly gone, and there are new causes of mutation, new kinds of selection, and vast migration. Today the numbers and distribution of the peoples of the world are due primarily to culture. Some people think the new conditions are so different that it is better no longer to use the word race or the word evolution, but I personally think this confuses more than it clarifies.

All this does not mean that evolution has stopped, because the new conditions will change gene frequencies, but the conditions which produced the old races are gone. In this crowded world of civilization and science, the claim has been made repeatedly that one or another of the races is superior to the others. Obviously, this argument cannot be based on the past; because something was useful in times past and was selected for under conditions which are now gone, does not mean that it will be useful in the present or in the future.

The essential point at issue is whether the abilities of large populations are so different that their capacity to participate in modern technical culture is affected. Remember in the first place that no race has evolved to fit the selective pressures of the modern world. Technical civilization is new and the races are old. Remember also that all the species of *Homo* have been adapting to the human way of life for many thousands of years. Tools even antedate our genus, and our human biological adaptation is the result of culture. Man and his capacity for culture have evolved together, as Dr. Dobzhansky has pointed out. All men are adapted to learn language—any language; to perform skillful tasks—a fabulous variety of tasks; to cooperate, to enjoy art; to practice religion, philosophy, and science.

Our species only survives in culture, and, in a profound sense, we are the product of the new selection pressures that came with culture.

Infinitely more is known about the language and culture of all the groups of mankind than is known about the biology of racial differences. We know that the members of every racial group have learned a vast variety of languages and ways of life. The interaction of genes and custom over the millennia has produced a species whose populations can learn to live in an amazing variety of complex cultural ways.

Racism is based on a profound misunderstanding of culture, of learning, and of the biology of the human species. The study of cultures should give a profound respect for the biology of man's capacity to learn. Much of the earlier discussion of racial inferiority centered on the discussion of intelligence; or, to put the matter more accurately, usually on that small part of biological intelligence which is measured by the IQ. In the earlier days of intelligence testing, there was a widespread belief that the tests revealed something which was genetically fixed within a rather narrow range. The whole climate of opinion that fostered this point of view has changed. At that time animals were regarded as primarily instinctive in their behavior, and the genes were supposed to exert their effects in an almost mechanical way, regardless of the environment. All this intellectual climate has changed. Learning has proved to be far more important in the behavior of many animal species, and the action of the complexes of genes is now known to be affected by the environment, as is, to a great degree, the performance that results from them. For example, Harlow has shown that monkeys learn to learn. Monkeys become test wise. They become skillful in the solution of tests—

so monkeys in Dr. Harlow's laboratories are spoken of as naive or as experienced in the use of tests. To suppose that humans cannot learn to take tests is to suppose that humans are rather less intelligent than monkeys.

Krech, Rosenzweig, and Bennett have shown that rats raised in an enriched environment are much more intelligent and efficient as maze-solvers than rats that have been given no opportunity to learn and to practice before the testing. To suppose that man would not learn through education to take tests more efficiently, is to suppose that our learning capacities are rather less than those of rats.

The human is born with less than a third of the adult brain capacity, and there is tremendous growth of the cortex after birth. There is possibly no mammalian species in which the environment has a longer and more direct effect on the central nervous system than man. We should expect, then, that test results are going to be more affected by the environment of man than in the case of any other animal. Deprivation studies of monkeys and chimpanzees and clinical investigations of man show that the lack of normal interpersonal environment may be devastating to the developing individual.

Today one approaches the study of intelligence expecting to find that environment is important. The intellectual background is very different from that of the '20's. The general results on testing may be briefly summarized as follows:

The average IQ of large groups is raised by education. I believe the most important data on this are the comparisons of the soldiers of World War I and of World War II. More than 80 per cent of the soldiers tested in World War II were above the mean of those tested in World War I. This means a wholesale massive improvement, judged by these tests, in the sons of the people who fought in World War I.

In the states where the least educational effort is made, the IQ is the lowest. In fact, as one looks at the review in Anastasi, it is exceedingly difficult to see why anyone ever thought that the IQ measured innate intelligence, and not the genetic constitution as modified in the family, in the schools, and by the general intellectual environment.

I would suggest that if the intelligence quotients of Negroes and Whites in this country are compared, the same rules be used for these comparisons as would be used for comparisons of the data between two groups of Whites. This may not seem a very extreme thing to suggest, but if you look at the literature, you will find that when two groups of Whites differ in their IQ's, the explanation of the difference is immediately sought in schooling, environment, economic positions of parents, and so on, but that when Negroes and Whites differ in precisely the same way the difference is said to be genetic.

Let me give you but one example of this. Klineberg showed years ago in excellent studies that the mean test scores of many Northern Negro groups were higher than those of certain groups of Southern Whites. When these findings were published, it was immediately suggested that there had been a differential migration and the more intelligent Negroes had moved to the North. But the mean of Northern Whites test results is above that of Southern Whites. Are we to believe that the intelligent Whites also moved to the North?

There is no way of telling what the IQ would be if equal opportunity were given to all racial and social groups. The group which is sociologically classified as Negro in the United States, about one-third of whose genes are of European origin, might well test ahead of the Whites. I am sometimes surprised to hear it stated that if Negroes were given an equal opportunity, their IQ would be the same as the Whites'. If one looks at the degree of social discrimination against Negroes and their lack of education, and also takes into account the tremendous amount of overlapping between the observed IQ's of both, one can make an equally good case that, given a comparable chance to that of the Whites, their IQ's would test out ahead. Of course, it would be absolutely unimportant in a democratic society if this were to be true, because the vast majority of individuals of both groups would be of comparable intelligence, whatever the mean of these intelligence tests would show.

We can generalize this point. All kinds of human performance—whether social, athletic, intellectual—are built on genetic and environmental elements. The level of all kinds of performance can be increased by improving the environmental situation so that every genetic constitution may be developed to its full capacity. Any kind of social discrimination against groups of people, whether these are races, castes, or classes, reduces the achievements of our species, of mankind.

The cost of discrimination is reflected in length of life. The Founding Fathers were wise to join life, liberty, and the pursuit of happiness, because these are intimately linked in the social and cultural system. Just as the restriction of social and economic opportunity reduces intelligence so it reduces length of life.

In 1900 the life expectancy of White males in the United States was 48 years, and in that same year the expectancy of a Negro male was 32 years; that is a difference of 50 per cent, or 16 years. By 1940 the difference had been reduced to ten years, and by 1958 to six. As the life expectancy of the Whites increased from 48 to 62 to 67 years, that of the Negroes increased from 32 to 52 to 61 years. They died of the same causes, but they died at different rates.

Discrimination, by denying equal social opportunity to the Negro, made his progress lag approximately 20 years behind that of the White. Somebody said to me, "Well, 61, 67, that's only six years." But it depends on whose six years it is. There are about 19 million people in this country sociologically classified as Negroes. If they die according to the death rate given above, approximately 100 million years of life will be lost owing to discrimination.

In 1958 the death rate for Negroes in the first year of life was 52 per thousand and for Whites 26. Thousands of Negro infants died unnecessarily. The social conscience is an extraordinary thing. A lynching stirs the whole community to action, yet only a single life is lost. Discrimination, through denying education, medical care, and economic progress, kills at a far higher rate. A ghetto of hatred kills more surely than a concentration camp, because it kills by accepted custom, and it kills every day in the year.

A few years ago in South Africa, the expectation of life for a Black man was 40 years, but it was 60 at the same time for a White man. At that time a White woman could expect 25 more years of life than a Black woman. Among the Blacks the women lived no longer than the men. People speak of the greater longevity of women, but this is only because of modern medicine. High birth rates, high infant mortality, high maternal mortality—these are the hallmarks of the history of mankind.

Of course there are biological differences between male and female, but whether a woman is allowed to vote, or the rate that she must die in childbirth, these are a matter of medical knowledge and of custom. Biological difference only expresses itself through the social system.

Who may live longer in the future—Whites or Negroes? There's no way of telling. Who may live longer in the future —males or females? There is no way of telling. These things are dependent on the progress in medical science and on the degree to which this progress is made available to all races and to both sexes.

When environment is important, the only way genetic difference may be determined is by equalizing the environment. If you believe in mankind, then you will want mankind to live on in an enriched environment. No one can tell what may be the ultimate length of life, but we do know that many people could live much longer if given a chance.

Whether we consider intelligence, or length of life, or happiness the genetic potential of a population is only realized in a social system. It is that system which gives life or death to its members, and in so doing changes the gene frequencies. We know of no society which has begun to realize the genetic potential of its members. We are the primitives living by antiquated customs in the midst of scientific progress. Races are products of the past. They are relics of times and conditions which have long ceased to exist.

Racism is equally a relic supported by no phase of modern science. We may not know how to interpret the form of the Mongoloid face, or why Rh° is of high incidence in Africa, but we do know the benefits of education and of economic progress. We know the price of discrimination is death, frustration, and hatred. We know that the roots of happiness lie in the biology of the whole species and that the potential of the species can only be realized in a culture, in a social system. It is knowledge and the social system which give life or take it away, and in so doing change the gene frequencies and continue the million-year-old interaction of culture and biology. Human biology finds its realization in a culturally determined way of life, and the infinite variety of genetic combinations can only express themselves efficiently in a free and open society.

References

Anastasi, Anne. 1958. *Differential psychology: Individual and group differences in behavior*. New York, Macmillan Co.

Blum, Harold F. 1961. Does the melanin pigment of human skin have adaptive value? *The Quarterly Review of Biology* 36:50–63.

Coon, Carleton S. 1962. *The Origin of Races*. New York, Knopf.

Dobzhansky, Theodosius. 1962. *Mankind Evolving: The Evolution of the Human Species.* New Haven and London, Yale University Press.

Dublin, Louis I., Alfred J. Lotka, and Mortimer Spiegelman. 1949. *Length of Life: A Study of the Life Table,* revised edition. New York, The Ronald Press.

Klineberg, Otto. 1935. *Race Differences.* New York and London, Harper & Brothers.

Krech, David, Mark R. Rosenzweig, and Edward L. Bennett. 1962. Relations between brain chemistry and problem-solving among rats raised in enriched and impoverished environments. *Journal of Comparative and Physiological Psychology* 55:801–807.

Glossary

Achondroplasia. Abnormality in conversion of cartilage into bone arising during fetal life, resulting in short legs and arms, relatively long body, big head, square nose with depressed bridge, and spade-like hands.

Albinism. Congenital absence of pigment in the skin and its appendages.

Alkaptonuria. Congenital disorder of protein metabolism, with excretion of alkapton (homogenistic acid) in urine. Inherited as a recessive in most cases, sometimes as a dominant.

Allele. Any of the various forms of a gene. Alleles occupy the same position (*locus*) on a given chromosome pair, influencing in different ways the same developmental process.

Allopatric. Groups of populations which do not occur together, and which exclude each other geographically are termed *allopatric populations*.

Base pair. There are four bases, each of which consists of an electropositive element or radical united with an acid to form a salt. These are contained in *DNA*, and occur as *base pairs*, as adenine-thymine and guanine-cytosine. In RNA thymine is replaced by uracil.

Brachydactyly. Shortness of the fingers.

Chromosome. One of a number of thread-shaped bodies situated in the nucleus of animal and plant cells and carrying the genes. A code center.

Cistron. The gene considered as the ultimate unit of physiological action having a specific functional role to perform, one duplicated by no nonallelic gene.

Cline. A gradient in a measurable genetic character within groups of animals or plants, and correlated with a gradient in the climate, geography or ecology of the groups.

Gene. The physical unit of heredity, a small region in a chromosome, consisting of a giant molecule or part of such a molecule, believed to consist mainly of deoxyribonucleic acid (DNA).

DNA or *Deoxyribonucleic acid.* The principal constituent of the gene, believed to be the material of heredity itself. DNA is thought to carry the master plans or code, containing the information that determines the order in which the amino acids fall into place in the protein molecule for which it is responsible.

Gene flow. Relating to the dissemination of genes from one population into another.

Gene frequency. Relating to the frequency of certain genes in certain populations.

Genetic drift or the Sewall Wright effect. The nonselective random distribution, extinction, or fixation of genes in a population.

Genetics. The branch of biology concerned with the manner in which inherited differences and resemblances come into being between similar organisms.

Genotype. The genetic constitution, determined by the number, types, and arrangement of genes.

Hardy-Weinberg Law. In a random mating (panmictic) population in which the pressures of mutation and selection, or other factors having similar effects upon gene frequencies, are absent or low, genotype frequencies, after the first generation of random mating will remain indefinitely unchanged, according to the formula $p^2 + 2pq + q^2$.

Locus. A particular place on a particular chromosome that always contains one kind of gene or one of a particular set of alleles.

Morphism. The form characteristic of an organism or group of organisms.

Mutation. A failure of precision in the basic property of self-copying in a gene, resulting in a transmissible hereditary modification in the expression of a trait. A mutation may arise from (a) a change in the number of chromosomes, (b) an alteration in a part of a chromosome, or (c) an alteration at a particular gene or locus on a chromosome.

Muton. The gene defined as the unit of mutation.

Natural selection. A short phrase for the effects of the differential reproduction of different types. The selection, by the environment, of certain genes or combination of genes in a population for survival.

Panmixis. Random mating in the absence of selection.

Phenotype. The manifest characteristics of the organism.

Polymorphism. Having several different forms. Used, for example, of such traits as the blood groups, occurring in fairly constant proportion among the members of a population or species.

Polypeptide. A peptide made up of an undetermined number of amino acids. Peptides are combinations of two or more amino acids, the carboxyl group of one being united with the amino acid group of the other, with the elimination of a molecule of water.

Population. Any contiguously distributed grouping of a single species that is characterized by both genetic and social continuity through one or more generations.

Recon. The gene as the ultimate unit of recombination, the chromosomal segment interchangeable but not divisible by crossing over.

Sickle cell. A genetically determined condition in which the red blood cells assume bizarre shapes, some resembling a sickle.

Species. A group of actually or potentially interbreeding natural populations that is reproductively isolated from other such groups.

Sympatric. Populations that occur together, whose areas of distribution overlap or coincide.

Index